A Guide to the Electricity at Work Regulations 1989

An Open Learning Course

LONDON: HMSO

Foreword

This is an open learning course on the Electricity at Work Regulations 1989. It has been produced by THELA* for Local Authority Inspectors and small businesses.

The course is intended to provide training for Inspectors and others who have duties under the Regulations, in the requirements of the Regulations, to aid in understanding the kinds of danger created by the use of electricity at work and to explain the principles behind the main techniques for preventing or reducing danger. It does not provide practical training for persons who work on electrical systems nor in identifying faults in a system. Additional training will be necessary for persons needing these skills.

The course should not be used as an authoritative interpretation of the Regulations. Practical guidance on the Regulations is contained in the "Memorandum of Guidance on the Electricity at Work Regulations 1989". This is available from Her Majesty's Stationery Bookshop. Detailed guidance on standards of electrical installation can be found in The Institution of Electrical Engineers Regulations for Electrical Installations (the IEE Wiring Regulations) obtainable from the IEE, PO Box 26, Hitchin, Herts, SG5 15A.

The Institution of Electrical Engineers was consulted during the preparation of this course.

THELA members include representatives from:

Health & Safety Executive;

Association of District Councils;

Association of Metropolitan Authorities;

Convention of Scottish Local Authorities;

Institution of Environmental Health Officers;

The Royal Environmental Health Institute of Scotland;

Institute of Safety & Public Protection;

Local Government Training Board;

North West Provincial Council.

*Training Sub-Committee of the Health and Safety Executive/Local Authority Enforcement Liaison Committee.

The New Regulations

The new Electricity at Work Regulations 1989 came into force on 1st April 1990 and apply to almost all work-places. The Regulations require precautions to be taken against the risk of death or personal injury from electricity in work activities. They replace the Electricity (Factories Act) Special Regulations 1908 to 1944.

The regulations impose duties on persons in respect of systems, electrical equipment, conductors and work activities on or near electrical equipment.

The Regulations state the principles of electrical safety in a form which may be applied to any electrical equipment and any work activity having a bearing on electrical safety. They apply to all electrical systems and equipment as defined in the Regulations whenever manufactured, purchased, installed or put into use. This includes equipment installed prior to the Regulations.

The Regulations place duties on duty holders in respect of the following:

- construction, maintenance and use of electrical systems;
- strength and capability of electrical equipment;
- adverse or hazardous environments;
- insulation, protection and placing of conductors;
- earthing or other suitable precautions;
- integrity of referenced (earthed) conductors;
- electrical connection;
- means of protecting systems from excess of current;
- means for cutting off the supply;
- means for ensuring precautions have been taken to isolate equipment made dead;
- work on or near live conductors;
- working space, access and lighting;
- persons to be competent in the prevention of danger and injury.

Practical guidance to the Regulations is given in the Memorandum of Guidance on the Electricity at Work Regulations 1989.

Where electrical equipment predates the Regulations this does not necessarily mean that the continued use of the equipment would be in contravention of them. Equipment made to a standard, such as a British Standard, or fixed equipment installed in accordance with the Institution of Electrical Engineers (IEE) Wiring Regulations, is likely to comply with the Regulations, provided that it has been properly maintained.

Guidance Relevant to the Electricity at Work Regulations 1989

The HSE has issued guidance notes and other publications giving detailed advice on such matters as, design of equipment, safe working practices, maintenance and repair of equipment, and installation practice for particular environments.

Guidance Note	Title	Regulations particularly relevant
	Guidance for Small Businesses on Electricity at Work	
	Memorandum of Guidance on the Electricity at Work Regulations 1989	
PM 29	Electrical Hazards from Steam/Water Cleaners	4, 6, 7, 8 and 10
PM 32	The Safe Use of Portable Electrical Apparatus	4, 6, 7, 8 9, 10, 11 and 12
PM 37	Electrical Installations in Motor Vehicle Repair Premises	4, 5, 6, 7, 8, 10, 11 12 and 16
PM 38	Selection and Use of Electric Handlamps	4, 6, 7, 8, 10 and 12
PM 51	Safety in the Use of Radio-frequency Dielectric Heating Equipment	4, 7, 8, 12, 13 and 16
PM 53	Emergency Private Generation: Electrical Safety	4, 5, 6, 7, 8, 9, 10, 11 and 12
PM 64	Electrical Safety in Arc Welding	4, 6, 7, 8, 10, 12, 14 and 16
GS 6	Avoidance of Danger from Overhead Electric Lines	4, 14, 15 and 16
GS 23	Electrical Safety in Schools	4, 6, 7, 8, 10, 11, 12, 14 and 16
GS 24	Electricity on Construction Sites	4 - 16 inclusive
GS 27	Protection against Electric Shock	4, 6, 7 and 8
GS 33	Avoiding Danger from Buried Electricity Cables	4, 14 and 16
GS 34	Electrical Safety in Departments of Electrical Engineering	4, 6, 7, 8, 12, 13, 14, 15 and 16
GS 37	Flexible Leads, Plugs, Sockets, etc.	4, 5, 6, 7, 8, 10 and 11
GS 38	Electrical Test Equipment for Use by Electricians	4, 5, 6, 7, 10, 14 and 16

Guidance Note	Title	Regulations particularly relevant
GS 44	Electrical Working Practices (in preparation)	4, 7, 12, 13, 14, 15 and 16
HS(G)13	Electrical Testing	4, 7, 12, 13, 14, 15 and 16
HS(G)22	Electrical Apparatus for Use in Potentially Explosive Atmospheres	4, 5 and 6
OP 10	Safety of Electrical Distribution Systems on Factory Premises	4, 5, 7, 8, 9, 11, 13 and
HS(G)38	Lighting at Work	4, 13, 14 and15

Status of the Memorandum of Guidance on the Electricity at Work Regulations 1989

The Memorandum is not an approved Code of Practice approved by the Health and Safety Commission under Section 16 of the Health and Safety at Work etc. Act 1974. Failure to comply with the procedures in the Memorandum is not in itself an offence. However, a court may view the failure as proof that the Regulation to which the provision relates has been contravened. The purpose of the Memorandum is to amplify the nature of the precautions in general terms in order to help achieve high standards of electrical safety in compliance with the duties involved.

The Institution of Electrical Engineers Regulations for Electrical Installations (the IEE Wiring Regulations)

The Institution of Electrical Engineers Regulations for Electrical Installation are non-statutory regulations. It is a Code of Practice widely recognised and accepted in the UK and compliance with them is likely to achieve compliance with the relevant requirements of the 1989 Regulations.

The IEE Wiring Regulations only apply to systems operating at voltages up to 1000 volts a.c. They do not apply to systems operating at higher voltages, nor to equipment on vehicles, systems for public electricity supply and explosion protection.

Installations would not fail to comply with the 1989 Regulations solely because they were installed in accordance with an earlier edition of the IEE Wiring Regulations which are now superseded by the current 15th Edition.

Other Statutory Regulations

The Electricity Supply Regulations 1988 impose requirements regarding installation and use of electric lines and apparatus by suppliers of electricity. These regulations are administered by the Engineering Inspectorate of the Electricity Division of the Department of Energy. They may impose requirements which are in addition to those of the Electricity at Work Regulations 1989.

The Building Standards (Scotland) Regulations 1981 and the Cinematograph (Safety) Regulations 1955 also remain in force.

The Low Voltage Electrical Equipment (Safety) Regulations 1989 apply only to the supply of electrically powered equipment.

How to use the open-learning course - Read this before you start.

This open-learning course comprises four modules, each made up of a varying number of units. Its intention is to enable you to teach yourself about the new Electricity at Work Regulations 1989 which came into force on April 1st 1990.

You can work through the modules at your own pace using whatever study method you feel suits you best. We have not stipulated a time for each module. The only guide you should use is your own level of understanding of the material. If you have difficulty with any section of the course, re-read it as many times as are necessary for you to familiarise yourself with its content. If you are to use your knowledge of the Regulations as a working tool it is essential that you should feel confident in your ability to apply it.

An open learning text is not intended to be simply read. It is effective as a teaching instrument because it is interactive. It requires you to do something at fairly regular intervals. You will not be expected to read through long pages of text before you are given a question to answer. However, if you choose to skip the numerous self-assessment questions which accompany each unit you will be putting yourself at a disadvantage. You will still learn something of the new legislation, but not as effectively as you would do if you worked through the exercises.

If you follow this simple rule, you will have a sound knowledge base on which your subsequent experience will allow you to build a thorough understanding of the Regulations and their implications.

Electricity - Basic Information

This package is concerned with the interpretation of a set of Regulations whose aim is to improve electrical safety. Although a number of definitions are given in the first module it might help you to set out some essential basic information at this stage. If you feel that you do not require this basic revision, skip this section and move on to Module 1.

Electricity is a form of energy. An electric current consists of a flow of negatively charged sub-atomic particles called **electrons**. The energy of an electric current depends upon two things: the number of electrons involved and the electrical 'pressure' which causes them to flow from one point in a conductor to another.

The flow of electrons is measured in **amperes** and the electrical 'pressure' in **volts**. Potential differences are mentioned in the text. The difference in electrical pressure between two points is called the potential difference and is again measured in volts.

An electric current will flow along a conductor if there is a potential difference between its two ends. This difference in pressure can be created by a chemical reaction, as in a battery, or by the movement of a conductor relative to a magnetic field. This means that the effect is the same if the conductor is moving through the magnetic field, or if it is stationary and the magnetic field is moving.

The zero point on the voltage scale is the potential of the mass of the Earth. This is always assumed to be at a potential of zero volts.

A current which flows only in one direction is called a **direct current** and is denoted by the letters d.c. If the direction of flow alters at regular intervals it is described as an **alternating current** and is denoted by the letters a.c. The domestic supply in this country is established at 240 volts a.c. at a frequency of 50 Hertz,(Hz). This means it changes direction 100 times a second (twice per cycle). Electricity is transmitted from the generating stations at a much higher voltage, 264kV or 400kV - (the 'k' is short for kilo, one thousand, so the transmission voltages are 264,000 volts or 400,000 volts). It is reduced to the lower (240 volt a.c.) domestic voltages by means of a **transformer**.

A transformer, in its simplest form, consists of an iron core on which are two windings. These windings are insulated both from the core and each other. The transformer will not function if a direct current is passed through it, the current must be alternating. The current to be transformed (raised or lowered in voltage) is passed through the **primary** winding. A moving magnetic field is created and a transformed alternating current appears in the **secondary** winding.

An alternating current can be converted to a direct current by being passed through a device called a **rectifier**. The direct current produced in this way may still have a fluctuating voltage. If the value of the voltage is plotted against time the graphs appears to 'ripple', like the surface of water. In this state it has some of the properties of alternating current. The term **ripple free** is used in the text which follows. It describes a true direct current with a constant voltage and no ripple.

An electric current, whether direct or alternating, must have a conductor through which to flow. Solid conductors of electricity are nearly all metals, (carbon, which is a non-metal, is a notable exception). Very poor conductors of electricity are called **insulators**. There must be a continuous circuit of conducting material through which the current can flow. The **resistance** to the flow of an electric current through a conductor depends upon its physical dimensions and the nature of the material from which it is made. However, when an alternating current flows there may be inductance and capacitance effects associated with the conductor which also affect the flow of current through it. The combination of the electrical resistance of the conductor and the resistance due to inductance and capacitance effects is referred to as the **impedance.** If the circuit is broken the current ceases to flow. This condition is described as an **open circuit**. We create an open circuit every time we switch off a light.

If a circuit is linked by a conductor, deliberately or accidentally, to an area of lower electrical potential, the current will flow to the lower potential instead of round the circuit. It is said to be **short-circuited.**

Such a short circuiting link may reduce the resistance to the flow of the electric current very significantly. The lower the resistance the greater the flow, and the resulting short circuit current may be very large. The short circuit current which would result if a particular point in a circuit was connected directly to earth is called the **fault level** at that point. The current which would flow is called the **fault current** and the new circuit created by the short circuit is called the **earth fault loop**. Remember if there is a break (open circuit) in the earth fault loop, no fault current would flow. If there was a high electrical resistance in the earth fault loop, only a small fault current would flow.

The fault currents are usually very large and potentially very damaging. The Regulations require any electrical equipment used in a system to be able to withstand the effects of foreseeable fault currents. Its **withstand properties** should be suitable for the function it is expected to fulfil.

The manufacturers of electrical equipment will usually give some indication of the withstand properties of their products. This usually takes the form of a statement indicating that it has been manufactured to meet the requirements of a particular standard. In this country **certified** equipment usually meets the standards set out in various British Standards.

Finally, in the text we make reference to line or phase conductors and neutral conductors. The domestic electricity supply is single phase. The neutral conductor is usually at a potential of zero volts, while the phase conductor has a potential of 240 volts. Think of the phase conductor as the 'live' wire in a circuit.

This revision of the basics has been very brief and if your memory is a little rusty you will probably need to re-read it more than once. You don't have to master it before you move on to the first module; you can always refer back to this section if you need to.

Symbols

You will encounter the following symbols in the circuit diagrams used to support the text. You should know what they represent so that you can understand what the diagrams are intended to show.

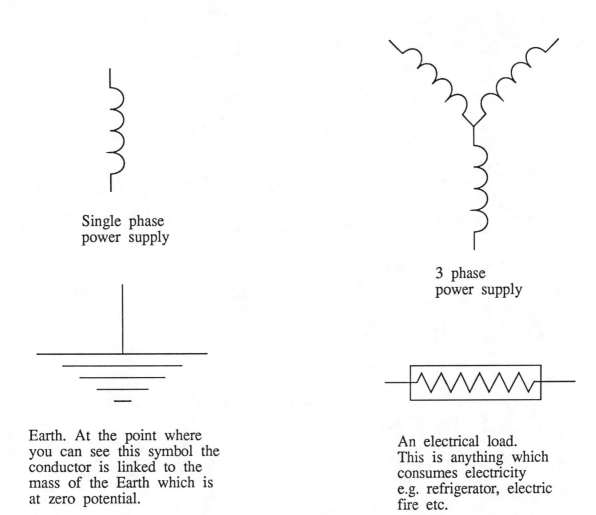

Single phase
power supply

3 phase
power supply

Earth. At the point where
you can see this symbol the
conductor is linked to the
mass of the Earth which is
at zero potential.

An electrical load.
This is anything which
consumes electricity
e.g. refrigerator, electric
fire etc.

Fuse

Fault

P = Phase = Line conductor.
N = Neutral conductor.
E = Earth conductor.

MODULE ONE

CONTENTS

Introduction

Module 1 of this open-learning text establishes the context in which the Electricity at Work Regulations 1989 are set.

Before we go on to examine the detailed requirements of the Regulations in Modules 2, 3 and 4, it is important that we establish:

i)   who has duties under the Regulations;

ii)   what levels of competence and experience are required of these people;

iii)   the work area covered by the Regulations and the provisions for exemption;

iv)   what defence might be successful against a charge of breaching the Regulations;

v)   the interpretation of the technical terms used throughout the Regulations.

Module 1 consists of two units. In Unit 1 we cover points(i) - (iv) listed above while Unit 2 is devoted entirely to the interpretation of the technical terms used in the Regulations.

UNIT 1

1.1.1. Aim

The aim of Unit 1 is to familiarise you with the requirements of Regulations 3, 16, 29, 30, 31, 32 and 33.

Objectives

When you have worked through this Unit you will be able to:

- list the categories of persons on whom the Regulations impose duties;

- explain the meaning of 'employer' and 'self employed' as used in the Regulations;

- define the terms 'absolute' and 'reasonably practicable' as they are used in the Regulations;

- describe the circumstances which might result in certain individuals not being allowed to carry out electrical work;

- give examples of what is meant by 'technical knowledge' and 'experience' within the context of these Regulations;

- describe the support which should be given to those allocated supervisory duties;

- state the employer's responsibility in respect of his employees' training and supervision;

- list those persons and things which can be exempted from a part or the whole of the Regulations;

- list those premises and activities to which the Regulations do not apply within the UK;

- list the revocations and modifications which were effected when the Regulations came into force on April 1, 1990;

- list the Regulations where a defence that the duty holder took all reasonable steps and exercised all due diligence to avoid committing an offence could be successful in criminal proceedings against an alleged breach.

1.1.2. Overview

This first Unit is divided into three sub-sections. The categories of persons on whom the Regulations lay specific duties, covered by Regulation 3, is the subject of the first section. Section 2 is concerned with competency which is dealt with by Regulation 16. This second section is followed by a Self-Assessment Question Test which gives you the opportunity to check your progress.

The application of the Regulations and the defence which can be offered against an alleged breach are covered in Section 3.

1.1.3. Section 1 - DUTIES

Regulation 3 identifies those categories of persons on whom the Regulations lay duties and indicates, in general terms, what those duties are.

1.1.3.1. Regulation 3:

Persons on whom duties are imposed by these Regulations.

1. *Except where otherwise expressly provided in these Regulations, it shall be the duty of every:*

    a) *employer and self-employed person to comply with the provisions of these Regulations in so far as they relate to matters which are within his control; and*

    b) *manager of a mine or quarry (within in either case the meaning of section 180 of the Mines and Quarries Act 1954[(a)]) to ensure that all requirements or prohibitions imposed by or under these Regulations are complied with in so far as they relate to the mine or quarry or part of a quarry of which he is the manager and to matters which are within his control.*

2. *It shall be the duty of every employee while at work:*

    a) *to co-operate with his employer so far as is necessary to enable any duty placed on that employer by the provisions of these Regulations to be complied with; and*

    b) *to comply with the provisions of these Regulations in so far as they relate to matters which are within his control.*

1.1.3.2. Employer:

An employer is any person or body who:

a) employs one or more individuals under a contract of employment or apprenticeship; or

b) provides training under the schemes to which the HSW Act applies through the Health and Safety (Training for Employment) Regulations 1988 (Statutory Instrument No. 1988/1222)

The contract of employment need not be in writing.

1.1.3.3. Self-employed

A self-employed person is an individual who works for gain or reward otherwise than under a contract of employment whether or not he employs others.

1.1.3.4. Employee

Regulation 3(2)(b) places the same duties on employees as are placed on the employer and the self-employed where the matters covered by the Regulations are under their control. However, the degree of responsibility borne by the employee cannot be as clearly defined as that of the employer and the self-employed. It should be remembered that trainees, as defined in Paragraph 1.1.3.2. are also classed as employees.

1.1.3.5. Control

The 'control' which any person exercises over the electrical safety in any particular circumstances will determine to what extent that person holds responsibilities under the Regulations to ensure that they are complied with.

This point is of particular importance because of the serious consequences which may result from the failure of any individual to carry out his responsibilities.

The term 'within his control' opens up the possibility of any individual, from any of the three categories, being held responsible for causing a dangerous situation which may arise in an electrical system beyond his own installation. This may be the case if the action the individual takes or fails to take within his own installation creates adverse effects elsewhere in the system.

Although managers of mines and quarries have similar duties imposed on them by these Regulations (Regulations 17 - 28 inc.), no further reference will be made to them in this course.

Some of the duties imposed by the Regulations are qualified by the phrase 'so far as is reasonably practicable'. Where 'reasonably practicable' is not used the requirement is absolute.

1.1.3.6. Reasonably Practicable

When this term is used the duty holder must assess and balance the risks of danger against the cost, time and effort involved in removing that danger. If the risk is small but the associated costs in money, time and effort are high, it may not be reasonably practicable to remove it. However, as the risk increases, the more difficult it becomes for the duty holder to show that it is not reasonably practicable to take action to eliminate it.

In the context of the Regulations where the risk is very often that of death, for example, from electrocution and where the nature of the precautions which can be taken are so often relatively simple and cheap, e.g. provide insulation, the level of duty to prevent that danger approaches that of an absolute duty.

1.1.3.7. Absolute

If a requirement is absolute then it must be met regardless of the time, cost and effort involved. However, the absolute requirements contained in the Regulations are subject to the defence outlined in Regulation 29 which is dealt with in paragraph 1.1.7.8. of this unit.

1.1.4. Section 2 - COMPETENCY

Regulation 16 is concerned with the competence of workers in situations which are potentially dangerous.

1.1.4.1. Regulation 16:

Persons to be competent to prevent danger and injury.

> *No person shall be engaged in any work activity where technical knowledge or experience is necessary to prevent danger or, where appropriate, injury, unless he possesses such knowledge or experience, or is under such degree of supervision as may be appropriate having regard to the nature of the work.*

The purpose of Regulation 16 is to ensure that individuals employed on electrical work do not cause danger to themselves or anybody else, or do not cause injury where danger cannot be prevented. The 'suitable precautions' referred to in Regulation 14 (see paragraph 1.1.4.6.), could include a competence check carried out before a worker is assigned a task that may be potentially hazardous.

The defence outlined in Regulation 29 is available in any proceedings for an offence under this Regulation.

1.1.4.2. Danger - Real and Potential

Regulation 16 applies to work activities on all electrical systems where danger exists or may arise. It does not actually have to be present for the Regulation to apply.

For example,where a person has to isolate some electrical equipment, before working on it, they will require sufficient technical knowledge or experience to prevent danger during the isolation. There will be no danger from the equipment during the work, provided that the isolation has been carried out properly; **danger will have been prevented but the person doing the work on the equipment must have sufficient technical knowledge or experience so as to prevent danger during that work, for example, by knowing which adjacent circuits may be live and being able to test to prove this, etc.**

The Regulation also covers those circumstances where danger is present, i.e. where there is a risk of injury. This could be work on live equipment using special techniques under the terms of Regulation 14. In these circumstances persons must possess sufficient technical knowledge or experience.

1.1.4.3. Technical Knowledge or Experience

The Regulation emphasises the need to possess appropriate technical knowledge or experience. Examples illustrating the scope of what might constitute technical knowledge or experience are:

a) adequate knowledge of electricity;
b) adequate experience of electrical work;
c) adequate understanding of the system to be worked on and practical experience of that class of system;
d) understanding of the hazards which may arise during the work and the precautions which need to be taken;
e) ability to recognise at all times, whether it is safe for the work to continue.

1.1.4.4. Preventive Action

Both employers and employees share a responsibility for safety.

i) **Employer's Responsibility**
   The employer should ensure that his workers receive appropriate training and instruction so that they understand the safe procedures which are relevant to their work, and/or they are adequately supervised.

ii) **Employee's Responsibility**
   All employees should comply with the instructions or rules set down by their employers to ensure that work is carried out safely.

1.1.4.5. Supervision

If supervision is necessary to ensure safe working then the following points should be kept in mind.

i) Those duty holders who are responsible for allocating supervision duties should make clear to the supervisors what the attendant responsibilities are.

ii) Where the risk is low, oral instructions may be adequate. However as the risk or complexity increases the point is reached where written instructions are required in order to ensure that they are understood and so can be rigorously applied.

Supervision need not be continuous. However, the degree of supervision required and the manner in which it is exercised to ensure that danger or injury is prevented should be decided by the duty holder.

In addition, Regulation 14 makes an indirect reference to the competence of people working on or near live conductors.

1.1.4.6. Regulation 14:

Work on or near live conductors.

*No person shall be engaged in any work activity on or so near any live **conductor** (other than one suitably covered with insulating material so as to prevent **danger**) that **danger** may arise unless -*

a) *it is unreasonable in all the circumstances for it to be dead; and*

b) *it is reasonable in all the circumstances for him to be at work on or near it while it is live; and*

c) ***suitable precautions (including where necessary the provision of suitable protective equipment) are taken to prevent injury.***

Suitable precautions should include the use of people who are properly trained and competent to work on live equipment safely. Regulation 14 is dealt with more fully in Module 4.

1.1.5. Self Assessment Question Test

We have now reached the point where you are given the opportunity to test your understanding of the material covered so far.

The test consists of 6 questions. When you have completed it you will find the answers to the questions on the pages immediately following.

1. SAQ - Duty Holders under the Regulations

Complete the following statement:

For the purposes of the Regulations, an employer is any person or body who:

a)   employs one or more individuals under a contract of employment or

_____ ;

or

b)   provides training under the schemes which the HSW Act applies through the

_____ .

2. SAQ - Duties of Employees

Indicate which of the following statements are true or false by ringing the appropriate letter:

a)   Employees share the same level of duty as their employers under the Regulations   T/F

b)   Employees may have some duties under the Regulations, depending on the circumstances.   T/F

c)   The duties of employees depend upon the level of control they exercise over electrical safety in a particular situation.   T/F

d)   Employees can only be responsible for those matters, subject to the Regulations, which are under their control.   T/F

3. SAQ - Extent of Duties under the Regulations

In situations subject to the Regulations where danger arises because of the action or inaction of individuals, are they still responsible if the danger is in some part of the system outside their own installation? Which of the following is the correct answer? Tick the appropriate box.

a) They are not responsible if the danger arises outside their own installations. ☐

b) They are responsible only if they are aware of the consequences of their actions. ☐

c) They are not responsible if they do not possess the knowledge which would make them aware of the consequences of their actions or inactions. ☐

d) They are responsible although the danger has arisen outside their own installations. ☐

4. SAQ - The Application of Regulation 16

Indicate which of the following statements are true or false by ringing the appropriate letter.

a) Regulation 16 applies to persons working on any electrical systems. T/F

b) Regulation 16 applies only to persons working on those electrical systems where work must be carried out on live conductors. T/F

c) Only persons working on those electrical systems which are dangerous or potentially dangerous are covered by Regulation 16. T/F

d) If a person is working on an electrical system which is safe, they are not covered by Regulation 16. T/F

5. SAQ - Technical Knowledge and Experience

Give THREE examples of what may be considered to be within the scope of 'technical knowledge or experience'. Use the space below for your answer.

_____

_____

_____

6. SAQ - Preventive Action

When work is being carried out on an electrical system which of the following statements is true? Ring T for true or F for false.

a) The employer is solely responsible for the employee's safety. T/F

b) Employees are solely responsible for their own safety. T/F

c) The responsibility for safety is shared by both employers and employees to the extent of their respective control. T/F

d) Sole responsibility must be allocated, but it depends on the circumstances. T/F

The answers to this test appear on the next page.

8

1. Response - SAQ - Duty Holders under the Regulations

Complete the following statement:

For the purposes of the Regulations, an employer is any person or body who:

a) employs one or more individuals under a contract of employment or **apprenticeship;**

or

b) provides training under the schemes to which the HSW Act applies through the **Health and Safety (Training for Employment) Regulations 1988.**

2. Response - SAQ - Responsibilities of Employees

a) Employees share an equal degree of responsibility with their employees under the Regulations.   T/**F**

b) Employees may have some degree of responsibility under the Regulations, depending on the circumstances.   **T**/F

c) The degree of responsibility employees hold depends upon the level of control they exercise over electrical safety in a particular situation.   **T**/F

d) Employees can only be responsible for those matters, subject to the Regulations, which are under their control.   **T**/F

3. Response - SAQ - Extent of Responsibility under the Regulations

In situations subject to the Regulations where danger arises because of the action or inaction of individuals, are they still responsible if the danger is in some part of the system outside their own installation? Which of the following is the correct answer? Tick the appropriate box.

a) They are not responsible if the danger arises outside their own installations.   ☐

b) They are responsible only if they are aware of the consequences of their actions.   ☐

c) They are not responsible if they do not possess the knowledge which would make them aware of the consequences of their actions or inactions.   ☐

d) They are responsible although the danger has arisen outside their own installations.   ☑

The correct answer is (d). They are responsible although the danger has arisen outside their own installations.

4. Response - SAQ - The Application of Regulation 16

a) Regulation 16 applies to persons working on all electrical systems   T/**F**

b) Regulation 16 applies only to persons working on those electrical systems where work must be carried out on live conductors   T/**F**

c) Only persons working on those electrical systems which are dangerous or potentially dangerous are covered by Regulation 16   **T**/F

d) If a person is working on an electrical system which is safe, they are not covered by Regulation 16.   T/**F**

5. Response - SAQ - Technical Knowledge and Experience

The examples of what may be considered to be appropriate 'technical knowledge or experience' given in the text are:

a) adequate knowledge of electricity;

b) adequate experience of electrical work;

c) adequate understanding of the system to be worked on and practical experience of that class of system;

d) understanding of the hazards which may arise during the work and the precautions which need to be taken;

e) ability to recognise, at all times, whether it is safe for the work to continue.

6. Response - SAQ - Preventive Action

When work is being carried out on an electrical system which of the following statements is true? Ring T for true or F for false.

a) The employer is solely responsible for the employee's safety.   T/**F**

b) Employees are solely responsible for their own safety.   T/**F**

c) The responsibility for safety is shared by both employers and employees to the extent of their respective control.   **T**/F

d) Sole responsibility must be allocated, but it depends on the circumstances.   T/**F**

Only (c) is true. When work is being carried out on an electrical system the responsibility for safety is shared by both employers and employees.

1.1.6. Summary Of Key Points

- The employer, the self-employed and the employee, have a duty to comply with the provision of the Electricity at Work Regulations 1989 insofar as they relate to matters within their control.

- The degree of 'control' which an employee may exercise over electrical safety will determine the degree of responsibility he or she holds under the Regulations.

- Some of the duties imposed by the Regulations are qualified by the term 'so far as is reasonably practicable.'

- Where the risk is death from electrocution, and the precautions are simple and cheap e.g. providing insulation, then the duty to prevent danger approaches an absolute duty.

- Regulation 16 applies to work activities at all electrical systems where danger exists or may arise. Danger does not actually have to be present for the Regulation to apply; where it is present the requirement is for competence to prevent injury.

- Anyone working on such a system should either possess the appropriate technical knowledge or experience to enable them to prevent danger/injury or be adequately supervised by a person possessing such knowledge.

- The duty holder responsible for allocating supervisory duties should ensure that each supervisor is clear about his/her responsibilities.

- As the degree of risk and complexity increases, consideration should be given to providing written instructions.

1.1.7. Section 3 - DEFENCE EXEMPTIONS, EXTENSIONS, DISAPPLICATION, REVOCATIONS,

This section covers Regulations 29 - 33 inclusive.

1.1.7.1. Regulation 29:

Defence:

> *In any proceedings for an offence consisting of a contravention of Regulations 4(4), 5, 8, 9, 10, 11, 12, 13, 14, 15, 16 or 25, it shall be a defence for any person to prove that he took all reasonable steps and exercised all due diligence to avoid the commission of that offence.*

Regulation 29 applies only in criminal proceedings. Regulation 25 applies only to mines.

Regulation 29 provides a defence for a duty holder who can establish that he took all reasonable steps and exercised all due diligence to avoid committing an offence under Regulations 4(4), 5,, 8, 9, 10, 11, 12, 13, 14, 15 or 16. These regulations impose absolute requirements on duty holders.

This defence only becomes relevant when it has been established that an offence has been committed in so far as the requirements of one of the Regulations have not been met.

1.1.7.2. Exemption Certificates

Regulation 30 deals with exemptions to the Regulations. The HSE have the power to grant general or special exemption to the duties imposed by the Regulations. Any exemption granted is subject to time limits and any other conditions the HSE consider to be appropriate. They are granted only in very exceptional circumstances.

1.1.7.3. Extension outside Great Britain

Regulation 31 is concerned with the extension of the Regulations outside Great Britain.

The Regulations apply outside Great Britain in the same way as the HSW Act. However within territorial waters they apply only to mines, construction work, loading and unloading ships, diving and ship repair. Oil rigs and pipelines are not subject to the Regulation.

Equipment which is manufactured in Great Britain but is installed or intended for use in those areas where the Regulations do not apply is not "equipment" for the purposes of the Regulations and so is not subject to them. However, if it is energised v/hile it is within Great Britain, e.g. in order to test it, it becomes subject to the Regulations during the period it is energised.

1.1.7.4. Disapplication of Duties

Regulation 32 is concerned with the disapplication of duties imposed by the Regulations.

The Regulations do not apply to those activities on a sea-going ship carried out by the crew under the direction of the ship's master.

The Regulations will apply to other activities carried out on ships, e.g. where a shore-based company carries out electrical work on a ship, so long as the ship remains in an area to which the Regulations apply, (Regulation 31).

The Regulations do not apply to any person in relation to an aircraft or hovercraft which is moving under its own power. The Regulations do apply to persons working on electrical equipment on other vehicles if the equipment may give rise to danger.

1.1.7.5. Revocations and Modifications

Regulation 33 deals with revocations and modifications which result from the Regulations.

The legislation revoked is specified in column 1 of part 1 of Schedule 2 to the Regulations. The Electricity (Factories Act) Special Regulations 1908 and 1944 are revoked completely.

Systems and equipment which were subject to provisions which have been revoked are now subject to these Regulations.

UNIT 2

1.2.1. Aim

The aim of this unit is to make you aware of the interpretation which should be put on the common technical terms used in the Regulations.

Objectives

When you have worked through this unit you will be able to:

- explain how the following terms should be interpreted for the purposes of the Electricity at Work Regulations 1989:

  i) systems;

  ii) electrical equipment;

  iii) conductor;

  iv) conductor in a system;

  v) circuit conductor;

  vi) danger;

  vii) injury;

  viii) isolation;

- describe how the body may be affected by the passage of an electric current through it;

- list the factors which influence the likely effect of an electric shock;

- describe how electric burns are caused;

- explain how fires may be caused by electricity;

- describe how arcing faults occur and the injuries which may result;

- explain how electricity can cause explosions;

- explain the meaning of 'charged/live' and 'dead', for the purposes of the Regulations.

1.2.2. Overview

This unit consists of two sections.

Section 1 explains the definitions of the basic technical terms you will encounter when reading the Regulations. It is important that you are aware of how the legal draughtsmen intended these terms to be interpreted. After each definition is given you will have the opportunity to test your understanding.

In Section 2 the nature of the injuries which can be suffered in electrical accidents are examined in more detail.

1.2.3. Section 1 - INTERPRETATION

The meaning of the basic technical terms used throughout the Regulations is given in Regulation 2.

1.2.3.1. Regulation 2: Interpretation

1. *In these Regulations unless the context otherwise requires:*

    *"circuit conductor" means any **conductor** in a **system** which is intended to carry electric current in normal conditions, or to be energised in normal conditions, and includes a combined neutral and earth conductor, but does not include a **conductor** provided solely to perform a protective function by connection to earth or other reference point;*

    *"conductor" means a **conductor** of electrical energy;*

Conductors

A conductor, for the purposes of the Regulations, is any substance which will conduct electricity. Such a substance may be a solid, a liquid, or a gas; it may be a conductor in one state and a non-conductor in another, e.g. molten glass conducts electricity, solid glass does not.

Circuit Conductors

A 'circuit conductor' is a conductor whose normal function is to carry load current or be energised.

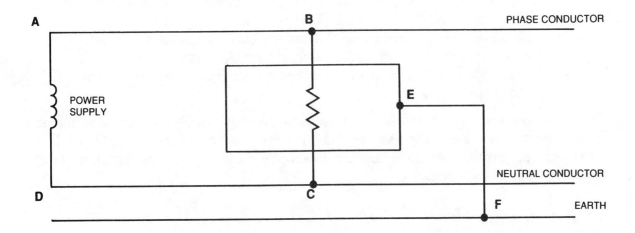

The diagram represents a piece of electrical equipment contained within an earthed steel case. It is intended that a current will flow through the phase conductor, the equipment and the neutral conductor, so AB, BC and CD are circuit conductors. Although, if an earth fault develops, a current may flow from the equipment case to earth, it is not intended that the conductor EF should normally carry a current. It is a conductor in a system, but not a circuit conductor.

1.2.3.2. Danger

"Danger" means risk of injury

The Regulations require duty holders to prevent danger or injury. In other words, to prevent the **risk of injury** or the **injury** itself. Why is it necessary to make the distinction?

Regulation 14 permits working on live conductors so long as certain precautions are strictly adhered to. In this case it is obviously impossible to eliminate the **risk of injury**, but the duty holder is required to ensure that no **injury** is suffered by anyone working on or near a live conductor.

1.2.3.3. Equipment

"electrical equipment" includes anything used, intended to be used or installed for use, to generate, provide, transmit, transform, rectify, convert, conduct, distribute, control, store, measure or use electrical energy;

For the purposes of the Regulations, electrical equipment includes every type of electrical equipment from bell wire to 400Kv overhead power cables, from a 1.5 volt dry battery to the largest power generator.

It is important that every type of equipment should be included if the Regulations are to be effective in improving electrical safety standards. The danger posed by an exposed conductor at a potential of several thousand volts is obvious. That posed by a pocket torch may be less obvious, but even the tiniest spark in an explosive atmosphere can have the most dire results.

1.2.3.4. Injury

"injury" means death or personal injury from electric shock, electric burn, electrical explosion or arcing, or from fire or explosion initiated by electrical energy, where any such death or injury is associated with the generation, provision, transmission, transformation, rectification, conversion, conduction, distribution, control, storage, measurement or use of electrical energy;

A comprehensive definition of injury is given but it must be remembered that the injury must be directly related to electricity. Any **secondary** injuries such as those sustained in a fall after receiving an electric shock are outside the scope of these Regulations. However, other legislation covers such incidents.

1.2.3.5. System

"system" means an electrical system in which all the electrical equipment is, or may be, electrically connected to a common source of electrical energy, and includes such source and such equipment.

The definition of an electrical system does not refer only to functional circuits. A system may contain one or many such circuits and is made up of all the electrical equipment and power sources which are connected electrically. This may not be the same as being physically connected, e.g. there are physical barriers between the windings of a transformer but they are electrically connected because electrical energy is transferred between them.

16

It follows, from this definition, that a system can be very extensive indeed and cover a very large geographical area. Within such a system many different people might exercise control over various sections of it. In this case, the Regulations place duties on these people only in respect of those related matters over which they exercise control.

A system does not have to be fixed, it can be portable, e.g. a portable generating set. It can form part of a mobile machine, e.g. the electrical system of a motor car. A system does not have to be energised, so long as it can be readily connected to a source of power, e.g. by the flick of a switch or the replacement of a fuse.

Equipment which is not, and cannot, be readily connected to a power source **is not part of a system.**

1.2.3.6. Live:

If a piece of equipment, system or part of system is live it has acquired a potential by being connected to a source of electricity.

1.2.3.7. Charged:

This has a different meaning from 'live'. It means that equipment, a system or part of a system, has acquired a charge **either** because it is live **or** because it has acquired a charge in some other way, e.g. an induced charge **or** it has retained or regained a charge although it may be disconnected from a system and its power source(s).

For equipment or a system to be **live,** it must be connected to a power source. However, if it is **charged** it may or may not be attached to a power source.

1.2.3.8. Dead:

If equipment, a system or part of a system is **dead**, it is neither **live** nor **charged**.

1.2.3.9. Isolated:

For equipment, a system or part of a system to be isolated it must be disconnected from all sources of electrical energy in such a way that it cannot be accidentally energised.

1.2.4. Self Assessment Question Test - Systems And Equipment

The definition of a 'system' and 'equipment' is given in Regulation 2. Use these two definitions to answer the following questions. Indicate your answer by ringing the appropriate letter, Y for 'yes' and N for 'no'.

1. SAQ - Systems and Equipment

1. Would a bicycle lamp constitute a system?   Y/N

2. Would the lighting circuit enclosed within the dotted line be
    considered to be a part of the system containing the power supply?   Y/N

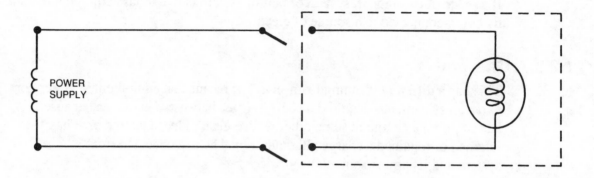

3. If a fuse blows in a domestic fuse box, so that the circuit it protects
    can no longer be energised, does the circuit remain a part of the
    house system?   Y/N

4. A lighting circuit is designed so that in the event of a power failure the
    system is energised using batteries. When the emergency power
    source is being used is the lighting circuit still regarded as a system
    for the purposes of the Regulations?   Y/N

5. Does it follow from the definition of a system that a single individual
    or corporate body must exercise control over it or have responsibility
    for it?   Y/N

6. A battery powered meter is used to test the heating element of an
    electric kettle. Does the heating element under test represent a part
    of a system?   Y/N

SAQ - Conductors, Conductors in a System, Circuit Conductors

The definitions of these terms are given in Regulation 2. Use them to answer the following questions.

Conductor

"Conductor" means a conductor of electrical energy.

2. SAQ - Conductors

Which of the following items is a conductor for the purposes of the Regulations? Ring Y for 'yes' and N for 'no'.

a)	The steel framework of a building,	Y/N
b)	A glass rod,	Y/N
c)	Sea water,	Y/N
d)	A length of telephone wire,	Y/N
e)	A steel crowbar,	Y/N
f)	A rubber sheet,	Y/N
g)	A brass screw,	Y/N
h)	A wooden chair leg.	Y/N

Conductors in a System

We have just dealt with conductors. Just to refresh your memory of what a system is for the purposes of the Regulations, we will repeat the definition again.

'System' means an electrical system in which all the electrical equipment is or may be, electrically connected to a common source of electrical energy, and includes such source and such equipment.

Use this definition to answer the following questions.

3. SAQ - Conductors in a System

Which of the labelled conductors in the circuit diagrams below are conductors in a system? Indicate your answer by ringing the appropriate letter, Y for 'yes' and N for 'no'.

a)   Y/N

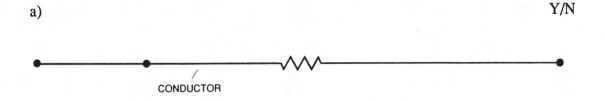

CONDUCTOR

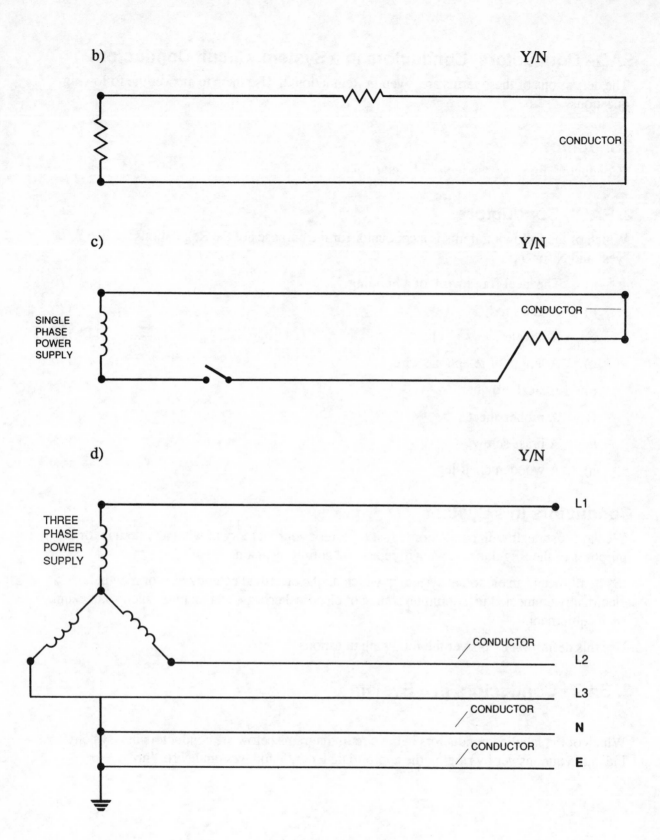

b)   Y/N

CONDUCTOR

c)   Y/N

SINGLE
PHASE
POWER
SUPPLY

CONDUCTOR

d)   Y/N

THREE
PHASE
POWER
SUPPLY

L1

CONDUCTOR

L2

L3

CONDUCTOR

N

CONDUCTOR

E

Conductors in a Circuit

Remember, 'circuit conductor' means any conductor in a system which is intended to carry electric current in normal conditions, or be energised in normal conditions, and includes a combined neutral and earth conductor, but does not include a conductor provided solely to perform a protective function by connection to earth or other reference point.

4. SAQ - Circuit Conductors

Which of the conductors indicated in the following diagrams are conductors in a circuit? Use the definition given above as a guide and again answer by ringing the appropriate letter.

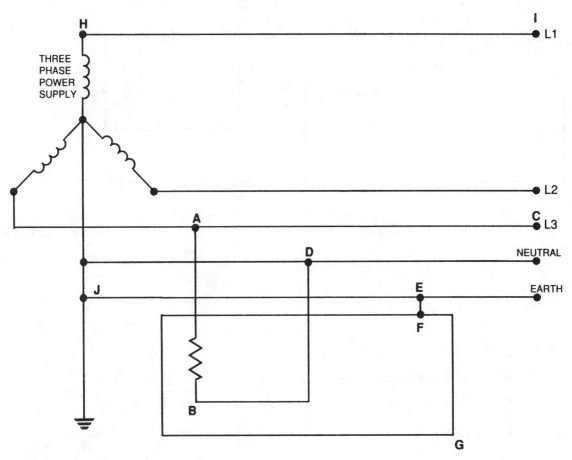

Is the conductor

a)	AB a circuit conductor?		Y/N
b)	AC a circuit conductor?		Y/N
c)	BD a circuit conductor?		Y/N
d)	EF a circuit conductor?		Y/N
e)	GF a circuit conductor?		Y/N
f)	HI a circuit conductor?		Y/N
g)	JE a circuit conductor?		Y/N

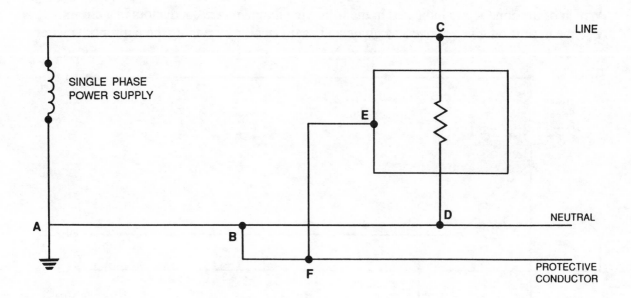

Is the conductor between

	h)	AB a circuit conductor?	Y/N
	i)	CD a circuit conductor?	Y/N
	j)	EF a circuit conductor?	Y/N

Danger and Injury

Before we discuss these two terms it might be appropriate to repeat the definitions given in Regulation 2.

"Danger"
> means risk of injury.

"Injury"
> means death or personal injury from electric shock, electric burn, electrical explosion or arcing, or from fire or explosion initiated by electrical energy, where any such death or injury is associated with the generation, provision, transmission, transformation, rectification, conversion, conduction, distribution, control, storage, measurement or use of electrical energy.

The Regulations make requirements to 'prevent danger' or 'prevent injury'.

22

5. SAQ - Danger and Injury

In Regulation 16, the duty holder is required 'to prevent danger or, where appropriate, injury.' Why is a distinction made between 'danger' and 'injury'. Use the example of an employee who is required to carry out work close to a live conductor which cannot be de-energised. Write your answer in the space below.

_____

_____

_____

_____

_____

Charged/Live and Dead

These terms are not given a special meaning for the purposes of the Regulations and so they take their ordinary meanings:

Live:

    'Live' refers to a conductor and means that it is at a higher electrical potential than its surroundings because it is connected to a source of electrical energy.

Charged:

    'Charged' means that the item has acquired a charge either because it is live or because it has become charged by other means or has retained or regained a charge due to capacitance effects although it may be disconnected from the rest of the system.

Dead:

    For a conductor to be 'dead' means that it is neither live nor charged.

6. SAQ - Live/Charged and Dead

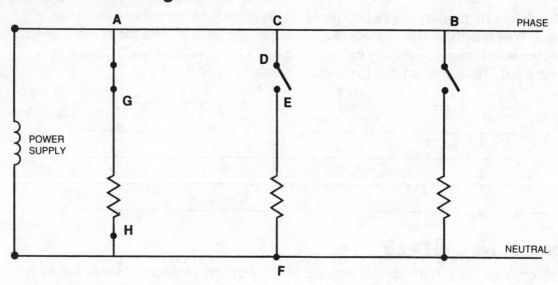

Indicate which of the labelled conductors in the circuit are live and which are dead by ringing the appropriate letter.

i)	Conductor AB	L/D
ii)	Conductor CD	L/D
iii)	Conductor EF	L/D
iv)	Conductor GH	L/D

Turn over the page when you wish to check your answers.

1. Response - SAQ - Systems And Equipment

1. Would a bicycle lamp constitute a system?

    The bicycle lamp contains electrical components which are all connected to the same source of energy, the battery, and so the lamp is a system.

2. Would the lighting circuit enclosed within the dotted line be considered to be a part of the system containing the power supply?

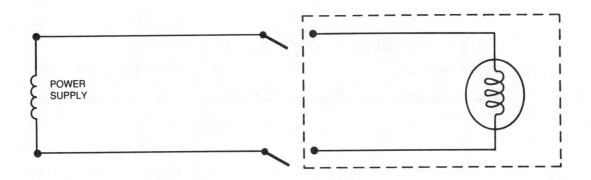

    The definition of 'system' includes equipment which, although not energised, may be electrically connected to a common source of electrical energy.

3. If a fuse blows in a domestic fuse box, so that the circuit it protects can no longer be energised, does the circuit remain a part of the house system?

    Again, although not energised, the circuit may be readily connected to the domestic electricity supply by replacing the fuse.

4. A lighting circuit is designed so that in the event of a power failure the system is energised using batteries. When the emergency power source is being used is the lighting circuit still regarded as a system for the purposes of the Regulations?

    The lighting circuit is still connected to a source of electrical energy and so it remains a system for the purposes of the Regulations.

5. Does it follow from the definition of a system that a single individual or corporate body must exercise control over it or have responsibility for it?

    In some cases the system may be an extensive electrical network covering a very large geographical area with many people controlling its various elements. Regulation 3 states that the Regulations place duties on these persons only in respect of those provisions of the Regulations which relate to matters which are within their control.

6.   A battery powered meter is used to test the heating element of an electric kettle. Does the heating element under test represent a part of a system?

In this case the equipment, (the heating element), is connected to a source of energy and so becomes part of a system.

2. Response - SAQ - Conductors

A conductor is anything which will conduct electrical energy. We are not confined by this definition to only those conductors which were designed to conduct electricity.

a)   The steel framework of a building   Ⓨ N

All metals are good conductors of electricity.

b)   A glass rod   Y Ⓝ

Glass in the solid state will not conduct electricity. It is used as an electrical insulator.

c)   Sea water   Ⓨ N

Sea water contains dissolved salts which gives rise to charged ions. This enables it to conduct electricity.

d)   A length of telephone wire   Ⓨ N

e)   A steel crowbar   Ⓨ N

f)   A rubber sheet   Y Ⓝ

Rubber is an insulator. It will not conduct electricity.

g)   A brass screw   Ⓨ N

h)   A wooden chair leg   Y Ⓝ

Wood acts as an electrical insulator.

3. Response - SAQ - Conductors in a System

a)   Y Ⓝ

CONDUCTOR

This circuit contains neither a power circuit nor can it be readily connected to one, so it is not a circuit.

b)

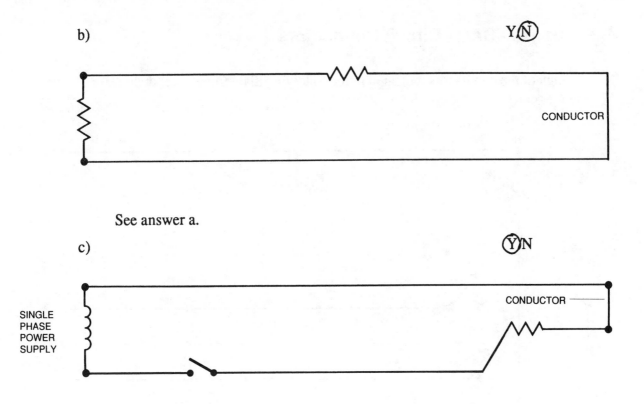

See answer a.

c)

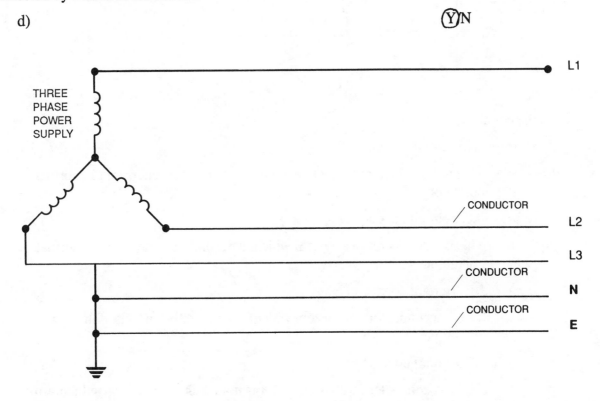

This circuit does contain a power source to which all the equipment it contains can be readily connected by means of the switch.

d)

All three of the labelled conductors are connected to a common source of electrical energy and so they are conductors in a system.

4. Response - SAQ - Circuit Conductors

Which of the conductors indicated in the following diagrams are conductors in a circuit?

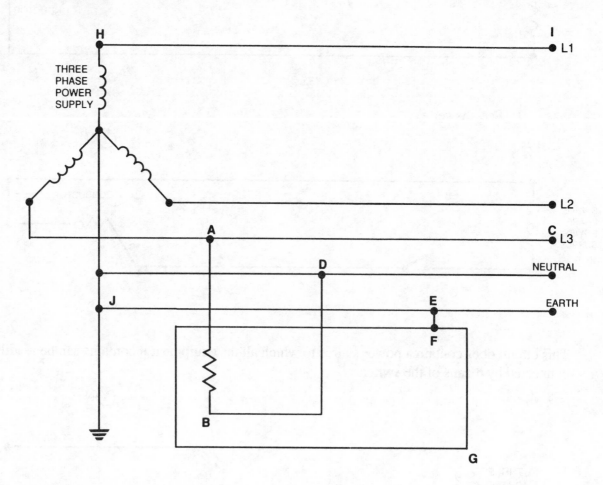

Is the conductor

a)   AB a circuit conductor?

This is a conductor in a system which is meant to be energised in normal conditions.

b)   AC a circuit conductor?

This is a conductor in a system which is meant to be energised in normal conditions.

c)   BD a circuit conductor?

This is a conductor in a system which is meant to be energised in normal conditions.

d)   EF a circuit conductor?

This is a conductor in a system but it is not meant to be energised in normal conditions.

e)   GF a circuit conductor?

This is a conductor in a system but it is not meant to be energised in normal conditions.

28

f) HI a circuit conductor?

This is a conductor in a system which is meant to be energised in normal conditions.

g) JE a circuit conductor?

As in (d), this is a conductor in a system but it is not meant to be energised in normal conditions.

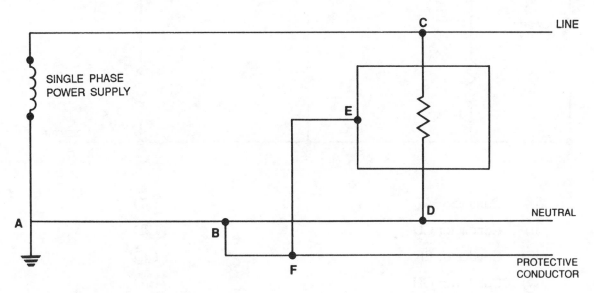

Is the conductor between

h) A and B a circuit conductor?

This is a conductor in a system which is meant to be energised in normal conditions.

i) C and D a circuit conductor?

This is a conductor in a system which is meant to be energised in normal conditions.

j) E and F a circuit conductor?

As in d, this is a conductor in a system but it is not meant to be energised in normal conditions.

5. Response - SAQ - Danger and Injury

In the example given, of an employee having to work close to a live conductor which cannot be switched off, it is obviously impossible for the employer to remove the danger. The risk of injury remains, so the Regulations impose the duty upon him to prevent injury.

The Regulations do not cover the situations where injuries are suffered as an indirect result of an electrical accident, e.g. a small electric shock causes an employee working high in a factory's roof space to drop the hammer he is holding, which falls and strikes a second employee on the shop floor below him.

This danger from falling objects is subject to other legal requirements.

In the rare instances when danger does not and cannot arise within an electrical system the Regulations still apply to it. In such a situation persons with duties under the Regulations are not required to take unnecessary precautions.

6. Response - SAQ - Live/Charged and Dead

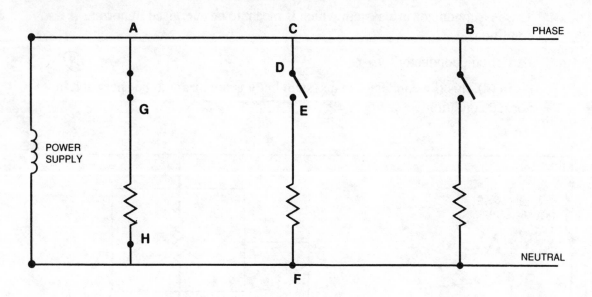

i)   Conductor AB   Ⓛ D

ii)   Conductor CD   Ⓛ D

iii)   Conductor EF   L Ⓓ

iv)   Conductor GH   Ⓛ D

1.2.5. Section 2: INJURY

1.2.5.1. Injury or death can result from:

i)   electric shock;

ii) electric burn;

iii) fires of electrical origin;

iv) electric arcing;

v)   explosions initiated or caused by electricity.

1.2.5.2. Electric Shock

It is very difficult to specify a voltage which will permit safe contact with a current carrying conductor under all conditions. However, it must always be assumed that the domestic electricity supply at a voltage of 240 volts a.c. is potentially fatal.

Once past the barrier of the skin which, when dry, has a relatively high resistance, the body offers a relatively low resistance and an electric current can take a multiplicity of paths through it. It is impossible to predict the intensity of the current, and the effect it may have, at any point within the body.

1.2.5.3. Effects of Electric Current passing through the Body

The body's electrical control system operates at a potential of a few millivolts. When a potential many times greater than this is applied across the body there may be a number of distressing effects. These can include any or all of the following:

- muscular contractions;
- respiratory failure;
- fibrillation of the heart;
- cardiac arrest;
- internal burns.

Any one of these may prove fatal.

1.2.5.4. Factors which affect the Nature and Severity of the Injury

The nature and severity of the injuries inflicted depends upon:

- the magnitude of the current passing through the body;
- the time for which the current flows;
- the path the current takes through the body;
- if the current is an alternating one, its frequency. The effects of electric shock are most acute at about the frequency of the public supply (50Hz).

1.2.5.5. Susceptibility to Electric Shock

Susceptibility to electric shock depends upon the nature of the surrounding environment. One which favours good electrical contact between a live conductor and the body will increase the likelihood of serious shock. Such environments might be found:

i)   in wet or damp conditions;

ii) where there is a high proportion of earthed metal, e.g. inside a steel tank in good electrical contact with the ground.

1.2.5.6. Electric Burns

Electric burns are caused by the heating effect of an electric current as it passes through the body. The greatest heating effect occurs at those points along the current path where the electrical resistance is greatest. Consequently, most burns occur on and within the skin. The wounds which result tend to be very localised, deep and slow healing and can result from a very brief passage of the current.

A transmitter of electrical energy radiated at radio frequencies, e.g. microwaves, does not have to be in contact with the body to cause burns. The energy is absorbed by the body and converted to heat which can damage tissue deep within the body. Severe damage can be inflicted by these sources before the victim is aware that they have been exposed to danger.

1.2.5.7. Fires of Electrical Origin

Fires may be started by electricity in a number of ways. The principal mechanisms are:

a)   overheating of cables and electric equipment due to overloading of conductors;

b)   leakage of current due to poor or inadequate electrical insulation;

c)   overheating of flammable materials placed too close to electrical equipment which is otherwise operating normally;

d)   the ignition of flammable materials by arcing or sparking of electrical equipment including the scattering of hot particles from electrical equipment.

1.2.5.8. Arcing

Arcing can cause burns and damage the eyes. The ultra-violet radiation generated by the arc can burn both the skin and the retina of the eye. There may be additional burn damage from radiated heat (infra-red radiation), molten metal and hot metal particles.

Arcing occurs when the potential of a conductor is great enough to create a conductive path across the intervening air gap or insulation material, between itself and a conductor of lower potential. In some cases a relatively minor short circuit can cause the air to ionise resulting in a major arcing accident.

Although arcing may only occur for very short periods (0.25 seconds or less) before the fault is cleared, very large amounts of energy may be involved. Consequently, severe burns or serious fires may result. The victim of an arc flashover may suffer very serious, sometimes fatal, burn injuries.

1.2.5.9. Explosion

Explosions cause severe injuries including burns, injuries from flying debris, and those caused when the body is thrown violently against some obstacle by the blast.

Explosions can arise in two ways.

1. Electrical explosions: These may occur when electrical equipment is subjected to excessive currents or prolonged internal arcing faults. The energy overload results in the sudden and catastrophic rupturing of the equipment.

2. The ignition of flammable gases, vapours, dusts or liquids by an electric spark, arc or the hot surface of electrical equipment

---

No voltage can be considered to be safe in ALL circumstances.

Although low voltages may reduce the risk of electric shock

there is no lower limit which will allow the safe use of electricity

in a potentially flammable environment without additional

precautions being taken.

1.2.6. Relevant Documents

The following documents give some further guidance:

(a) Health and Safety Executive Guidance Note GS27. Protection against electric shock;

(b) International Electrotechnical Commission Publication (IEC) 479. Effects of current passing through the human body. Also published as British Standard PD6519;

(c) The Institution of Electrical Engineers Regulations for Electrical Installations (the IEE Wiring Regulations);

(d) IEC Guide 105. Principles concerning the safety of equipment electrically connected to a telecommunications network.

1.2.7. Self Assessment Question Test

1. SAQ - Electric Shock

Tick the factors which influence the nature and severity of the injuries which can be inflicted by electricity.

- Magnitude of current
- Duration of flow
- Path through the body
- Electrical resistance of the body
- Frequency of current (if alternating)
- The immediate environment

2. SAQ - Fires of Electrical Origin

Indicate which of the following statements are true and which are false by ringing the appropriate letter.

a) As the electric current in a conductor decreases its heating effect increases.   T/F

b) A fire might result if the electrical insulation around a conductor is reduced.   T/F

c) If flammable material is placed close to electrical equipment it will eventually begin to burn.   T/F

3. SAQ - Arcing

Complete the following statement by deleting the words which are inappropriate.

Arcing faults can arise if the potential of (an insulator/a conductor) is (low, great) enough to create (an insulation barrier/a conductive path) across the air gap or through the insulation placed between itself and another (insulator/conductor) at a (lower/higher potential).

4. SAQ - Explosions

Electrical explosions may result from:

a) the ignition of flammable substances;

b) high surface temperatures of electrical equipment;

c) the violent and catastrophic failure of electrical equipment;

d) the flow of excessively high currents through conductors.

Which of the above statements is correct? Indicate your choice with a tick.

The answers to these questions are given on the next page.

1. Response - SAQ - Electric Shock

- Magnitude of current
- Duration of flow
- Path through the body
- Electrical resistance of the body
- Frequency of current (if alternating)
- The immediate environment

All of the factors listed influence the nature and severity of the injuries which can be inflicted by electricity.

2. Response - SAQ - Fire Of Electrical Origin

Indicate which of the following statements are true and which are false by ringing the appropriate letter.

a) As the electric current in a conductor decreases its heating effect increases. T/**F**

This is false. As the electrical loading of a conductor increases the heating effect increases.

b) A fire might result if the electrical insulation around a conductor is reduced. **T**/F

This is true. As the insulation is reduced the risk of leakage currents grows. These currents can give rise to a heating effect and the risk of fire.

c) If flammable material is placed close to electrical equipment it will eventually begin to burn. T/**F**

This is false. The risk of fire exists only if the equipment is generating heat and if the temperature of the material is raised to the point where it will spontaneously combust.

3. Response - SAQ - Arcing

The statement should read:

Arcing faults can arise if the potential of a conductor is great enough to create a conductive path across the air gap or through the insulation placed between itself and another conductor at a lower potential.

4. Response - SAQ - Explosions

The correct answer is (d). Electrical explosions may result from the flow of excessively high currents through conductors. Option (a) may give rise to an explosion but it would not be classed as electrical. High surface temperatures (b) may give rise to a similar type of explosion. Option (c) represents the effect of an electrical explosion rather than the cause of one.

1.2.8. Summary Of The Key Points

- 'System' means an electrical system in which all electrical equipment is connected to a common source of electrical energy and includes the source.

- Electrical equipment includes any thing used, intended to be used or installed for use in an electrical system.

- A circuit conductor is a conductor which is intended to be energised under normal conditions.

- Danger means risk of injury.

- Injury for the purposes of the Regulations are those which are caused by electricity. These include:

  i)   electric shock;

  ii) electric burn;

  iii) fires of electrical origin;

  iv) electric arcing;

  v)   explosions initiated or caused by electricity.

1.2.9. End Test

1.   What duties do the Regulations impose upon the employee?

2.   How can the absolute duties imposed by the Regulations be distinguished from those which are not?

3.   If a duty imposed by the Regulations is not absolute, under what circumstances may it approach that of an absolute duty?

4.   What is the purpose of Regulation 16?

5.   When is equipment manufactured in Great Britain but intended to be installed abroad regarded as equipment for the purposes of the Regulations?

6.   How do the Regulations define a conductor?

7.   What is the difference between a conductor and a conductor in a circuit?

8.   What is the definition of 'danger' given in the Regulations?

9.   List FOUR categories of injury covered by the Regulations.

10. What are the basic requirements of a system as defined in the Regulations?

11. Where in the body is the highest electrical resistance usually encountered?

12. Electrical equipment may explode if excessive currents are passed through it. In what other circumstance may such equipment explode electrically?

13. What voltage limit might be regarded as safe in a potentially flammable atmosphere?

End Test - Answers

1. What duties do the Regulations impose upon the employee?

Regulation 3(2)(b) places the same duties on employees as are placed on the employer and the self-employed where the matters covered by the Regulations are under their control. The degree of control they exercise will determine to what extent they are responsible.

2. How can the absolute duties imposed by the Regulations be distinguished from those which are not?

The duties which are **not** absolute are qualified by the words, 'so far as is reasonably practicable'.

3. If a duty imposed by the Regulations is not absolute, under what circumstances may it approach that of an absolute duty?

If the risk of death or injury is very great but the measures necessary to remove the risk are cheap and easy to install, the duty to eliminate the risk is virtually absolute.

4. What is the purpose of Regulation 16?

The purpose of Regulation 16 is to ensure that individuals employed on electrical work do not cause danger to themselves or anybody else.

5. When is equipment manufactured in Great Britain but intended to be installed abroad regarded as equipment for the purposes of the Regulations?

Normally, it would not be regarded as equipment. However, if it is energised at any time while it is in the area controlled by the Regulations it is regarded as such, but only so long as it is energised.

6. How do the Regulations define a conductor?

The Regulations regard any substance, solid, liquid or gas which is capable of conducting electricity as a conductor, whether or not it is intended that it should do so.

7. What is the difference between a conductor and a conductor in a circuit?

A conductor is a substance which is capable of conducting electricity whether it is intended that it should do so or not. A conductor in a circuit is a conductor which it is intended should normally carry load current or be energised.

8. What is the definition of 'danger' given in the Regulations?

Danger is defined as the risk of injury.

9.   List FOUR categories of injury covered by the Regulations.

Your list should include any FOUR of the following:

        a)   electric shock;

        b)   electric burn;

        c)   electric arcing;

        d)   electrical explosion;

        e)   injuries caused by fire or explosion initiated by electricity.

10.   What are the basic requirements of a system as defined in the Regulations?

All the equipment in a system must be connected to a power source or sources or must be capable of being readily connected to such a source or sources.

11.   Where in the body is the highest electrical resistance usually encountered?

The highest electrical resistance is usually encountered in the skin. Although internal burning can occur, most burns are concentrated within the skin layer where the electric current enters and leaves the body.

12.   Electrical equipment may explode if excessive currents are passed through it. In what other circumstance may such equipment explode electrically?

Electrical equipment may explode if there is prolonged internal arcing.

13.   What voltage limit might be regarded as safe in a potentially flammable atmosphere?

No voltage can be regarded as safe. Even the tiniest spark can ignite a flammable mixture.

MODULE TWO

CONTENTS

Module 2   **Page No.**

Introduction

The purpose of this module is to prepare the ground for the study of Regulations 4 to 15 inclusive, which are the subject of Modules 3 and 4.

You will find them more meaningful if you are aware of the causes and nature of the electrical hazards which the Regulations are intended to control.

We briefly reviewed the types of hazard which might arise and the injuries associated with them in Module 1. This review will now be extended to include both the common causes of these hazards and the measures taken to eliminate them.

UNIT 1

2.1.1. Aim

The aim of this module is to familiarise you with the hazards which can arise from the use of electricity.

Objectives

When you have worked through this unit you will be able to:

- describe the conditions which must exist for a person to be electrocuted;
- explain how the conditions might arise;
- give examples of situations where the risk of electrocution is present;
- explain how electricity might start fires;
- give examples of the situations where there is a high risk of fire and explosion;
- outline the precautions which are taken to remove or reduce the risk of electrical hazards;
- list the Regulations which are aimed at preventing danger.

2.1.2. Overview

This module consists of one unit. It is concerned with electric shock, electric burn, arcing, and the danger of fire and explosion where electricity is the source of ignition.

The conditions which must exist before electricity becomes dangerous are established first. This is followed by a consideration of how these conditions may arise and the measures taken to either:

i)   prevent the conditions developing;

    or

ii)   remove any danger if a situation becomes hazardous.

You will be able to monitor your progress with the help of self-assessment tests.

2.1.3. How Electrical Hazards Arise

An electrical system may be dangerous either because it contains a hazard or it is being used or worked on in a dangerous way.

The hazard may be known. In this case death or injury may still result because of a lack of knowledge/expertise or poor working practices. More often, those using or in contact with the system are unaware of the danger.

These hazards arise for a number of reasons. They may have been inadvertently built into a system through poor design or by the use of inappropriate or defective equipment. On the other hand, they may be the result of damage which has gone undetected because of poor maintenance.

In Module 1 we listed the dangers which could result in death or injury. These were:

- a)   electric shock;
- b)   electric burn;
- c)   arcing;
- d)   electrical explosion;
- e)   fire or explosion initiated by electrical energy.

We will look at each in turn and the measures taken to prevent them happening.

2.1.4. Electric Shock

2.1.4.1. The conditions necessary for electric shock to occur

There are two general categories of accident which involve electric shock.

In the first, the victim comes into contact with a live, uninsulated conductor. This is direct contact. However, in the case of kilo voltages, the victim does not have to make actual physical contact with the conductor. The electricity can 'jump' across the distance separating them, depending upon a number of factors including voltage, distance, shape of conductor and humidity.

In the second, the conductor which the victim touches does not normally carry an electric charge. It has been made live by being brought into contact with a live uninsulated conductor. This is indirect contact.

In both cases the victim is simultaneously in contact with another conductor which is at a different potential. Usually, the greater the potential difference, the larger the current flowing through the victim's body and the more pronounced the effects of shock. The time for which the current flows has a significant influence on the likelihood of death.

In most cases of electrocution the conductor with the lower potential is earth, which is assumed to have zero potential. How much current flows through the victim's body depends on the voltage and how good an electrical contact has been made. Someone standing barefoot on wet ground, or holding a metal object firmly embedded in the earth, will make good electrical contact with it, and will run the risk of receiving a dangerous electric shock.

In the examples we have just given, if the wet foot were inside a rubber boot or the hand inside a dry leather gauntlet, (both of which are poor electrical conductors) the risk of dangerous shock would be much reduced.

We have emphasised contact directly or indirectly with the earth and this is important. If the surface upon which someone is standing prevents them being in direct contact with the earth and is also a poor electrical conductor, e.g. a rubber mat, then any shock current will be small, perhaps so small that they cannot even feel it. Remember, as a rough rule of thumb, metals and most liquids are good conductors of electricity; non-metals are mostly poor conductors, (carbon is a notable exception).

2.1.4.2. Lethal Electrical Potentials

In Module 1 it was stated that 240 volt (50Hz) a.c. should always be regarded as being a lethal potential.

Experience has shown that systems operating at a potential of 50 volts a.c. or 120 volts (ripple free) direct (d.c.) are comparatively safe. It must always be remembered that environments which favour the conduction of electricity, e.g. wet, damp, or containing a high proportion of metal, might make even these 'safe' potentials dangerous. The size of the current associated with any electrical potential has a direct bearing on the sensation of shock it will produce. Most people will be aware of the presence of a potential large enough to produce a sensation if a current of 1 milliamp flows. However, if the current is raised to 100 milliamps the resulting shock might quickly prove fatal.

The ripple on a direct current is caused by a varying peak voltage which may be dangerous. At low voltages alternating current presents a greater hazard than direct current because of its effect on the heart.

In dry, cool conditions, when body resistance is not lowered by sweating, no precautions are usually required to prevent contact, so long as the potential does not exceed 25 volts a.c. or 60 volts (ripple free) d.c. These figures would have to be lowered to achieve the same level of safety if the environment was highly conducting, e.g. damp, wet or containing a high proportion of metal.

2.1.4.3. Self Assessment Question Test

1. SAQ - The conditions necessary for electric shock to occur

In which of the following situations would you be most vulnerable to electrocution because some part of your body would be at zero (earth) potential? Tick your choice.

a) Standing with wet feet on a dry, rubber mat.

b) Standing on a hard, dry clay surface, wearing rubber boots while holding a metal fence post which is being driven into the ground.

c) Sitting on a wooden chair, with your feet in a plastic bowl, half full of warm salt water.

d) Standing on a pair of wooden step ladders nailing a notice to a wooden pylon carrying an overhead power line.

2. SAQ - Dangerous potentials

Which of the potentials listed below would not usually require precautions to be taken to prevent direct contact? Indicate your choices with a tick.

a) 25 volts alternating current.

b) 25 volts (ripple free) direct current.

c) 60 volts alternating current.

d) 60 volts (ripple free) direct current.

3. SAQ - The likelihood of an electrical potential causing death

List the factors which influence the likelihood of an electrical potential causing death. Do not take into account the health/fitness of the potential victim.

_____

_____

_____

_____

The answers to these questions begin on the next page.

1. Response - SAQ -   The conditions necessary for electric shock to occur

In which of the following situations would you be vulnerable to electrocution because some part of your body would be at zero (earth) potential?

    a)   Standing with wet feet on a dry, rubber bath mat.

You would not be vulnerable to shock in this situation. Although your feet are wet you are insulated from the ground by the rubber mat.

    b)   Standing on a hard, dry clay surface, wearing rubber boots while holding a metal fence post which is being driven into the ground.

You would be vulnerable to shock in this situation. Although you are wearing rubber boots, which provide good insulation, your hand is in good electrical contact with the earth via the metal fence post.

    c)   Sitting on a wooden chair, with your feet in a plastic bowl, half full of warm salt water.

You would not be vulnerable in this situation. The wooden chair would act as an insulator. Salt water is a good conductor, but both the water and your feet are insulated from the earth by the plastic bowl which is a poor conductor.

    d)   Standing on a pair of wooden step ladders nailing a notice to a wooden pylon carrying an overhead power line.

You would not be vulnerable in this situation. The wooden steps would act as an insulator. Although you would be in contact with the wooden pole, which is set in the earth, its insulating properties when dry would ensure you are not in electrical contact with the earth.

2. Response - SAQ -   Dangerous potentials

Which of the potentials listed below would not usually require precautions to be taken to prevent direct contact?

No precautions against direct contact would usually be necessary in the case of:

    a)   25 volts alternating current.

    b)   25 volts (ripple free) direct current.

    d)   60 volts (ripple free) direct current.

Precautions would be necessary for (c) - 60 volts alternating current.

3. Response - SAQ -   The likelihood of an electrical potential causing death

List the factors which influence the lethality of an electrical potential. Do not take into account the health/fitness of the potential victim.

- its size;
- the time for which it is applied;
- the environment in which it is applied.

2.1.4.4. Summary Of Key Points

- Electrocution cannot occur unless the victim is simultaneously in contact with conductors which are at significantly different potentials. The victim's body then provides a path for a current to flow between the conductors.

- A person standing on the ground is not necessarily at earth potential. S/he may be insulated from the earth by footwear or the floor covering. Electrical contact with the earth must exist before any part of his/her body is at earth potential.

- In dry conditions, no special precautions are required to prevent contact with conductors at potentials not greater than 25 volts a.c. or 60 volts (ripple free) d.c.

2.1.5. How the danger of shock may arise

There are two general circumstances where the danger of electric shock can arise.

i)   A live conductor is exposed so that contact can be made with it directly. This can arise if the insulation protecting live equipment is removed or damaged or if the cover shielding exposed live conductors is removed.

ii)   A live conductor is exposed and is brought into contact with a second conductor which is not energised in normal circumstances. The second conductor, which can be solid or liquid, is then made live, so that anyone making contact with it runs the risk of electrocution. This circumstance can arise from (i) if the exposed conductor is then brought into contact with conducting material.

Both may result from:

a)   poor maintenance of electrical equipment; this can be eliminated completely by good planning;

b)   exposure of equipment to damage or improper use; this may be difficult, even impossible to eliminate altogether, but again good planning will help reduce the number of accidents arising from this cause.

Equipment may be damaged when it is exposed to:

a)   abrasion/impact;

b)   repeated stress;

c)   a hostile environment.

2.1.5.1. Abrasion/Impact

Regulation 7 is concerned with the insulation, protection and placing of conductors.

Cables which trail along the ground in an area where there is movement of personnel and/or vehicles, e.g. a construction site, or a maintenance department, will be at risk unless steps are taken to protect them. Electric cables connected to portable tools are an example of electrical equipment prone to this kind of damage.

Protecting Cables against Abrasion/Impact

Protective measures include:

i)   enclosing the cable within a protective cover;

ii)   burying it below ground level or raising it above;

iii)   using cable which is armoured.

Circumstances will dictate which measure or measures should be adopted to effect the necessary degree of protection.

Appendices 9, 10 and 11 of the IEE Wiring Regulations give comprehensive guidance on the choice and installation of electric cables.

2.1.5.2. Repeated Stress

Flexible cables provide a good example of a conductor prone to damage from repeated stress.

Most stress will occur at the point where the cable enters a rigid joint, e.g. at a plug or cable connector. The conductors in flexible cables are made up of relatively large numbers of thin strands but fatigue damage may still occur not only to the metal conductors but also in the insulation cover and sheathing if the cable is repeatedly flexed in one place.

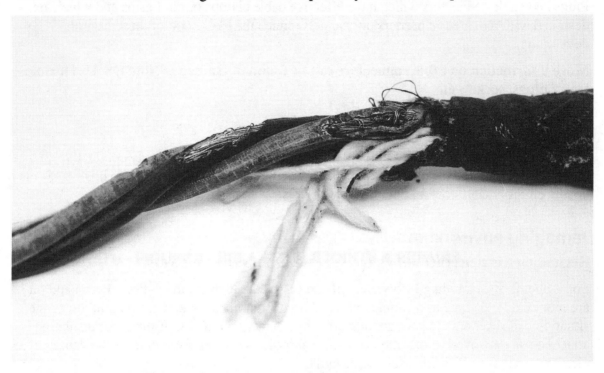

Protecting cables against repeated stress

Regulation 10 is concerned with connections in electrical systems

Where it is impossible to avoid rigid connections to flexible cables, a supportive resilient sleeve should be used.

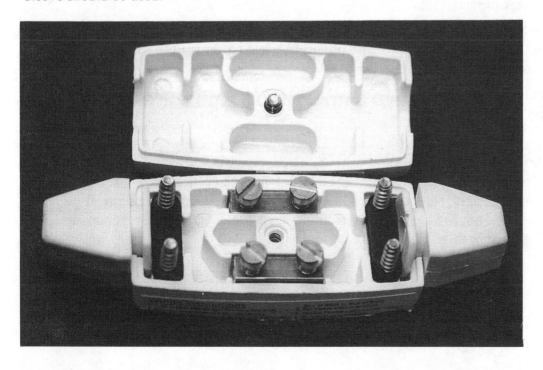

Cable joints are also subjected to tensile stress and, unless arrangements are made to combat this, individual wires can be pulled loose from their terminals leaving them free to make accidental contact. The precaution usually employed is a cable clamp within the connector which takes any tensile stress applied to the cable. Failure to secure cables in this way is a common cause of faults which give rise to the danger of electrocution as well as other hazards.

Plugs and cable connectors which have effective cable clamps or cord grips and which are designed with moulded-in barriers or channels reduce the likelihood of these hazards developing.

More information on cable connectors can be found in Guidance Note GS 37 Flexible leads, plugs, sockets etc

2.1.5.3. Hostile Environments

Environments which can damage electrical equipment or which are highly conductive so that any hazard arising from a fault is greatly magnified, must be considered to be hostile. Some hostile environments contain both dangers.

Damaging environments

Regulation 6 is concerned with adverse or hazardous environments.

Some chemicals, including P solvents, oil and petrol can damage insulation. Petrol and oil are more likely to come into contact with electrical equipment in garages than in most other situations. Rubber and plastics are degraded by contact with them. If the cable insulation is attacked and destroyed so that the conductors it protects are exposed, there is the danger of electrocution, as well as other related hazards.

Protecting Cables in Damaging Environments

Care must be taken in the selection and positioning of cables in such hostile environments to minimise these dangers.

Guidance Note PM37 'Electrical installations in motor vehicle repair premises' gives advice on the protection of cables and other electrical equipment in the hostile environments found in garages.

Additional advice is given in Guidance Note PM32, 'The safe use of portable electrical apparatus'.

Highly Conductive Environments

Damp, wet environments are highly conducting and these can be found, for example, in kitchens and in garages, particularly where vehicles are washed. Ideally, electrical equipment should not be used in these conditions at all. For example, wherever possible, hand tools should be driven by compressed air instead.

Protecting cables and associated equipment against highly conductive environments

Regulation 6 is relevant to these situations.

If electrical equipment must be used in damp or wet environments, every care must be taken to ensure that all connectors and plugs are water-proof.

Apparatus should be protected against hostile environmental conditions. A coded classification 'The Index of Protection' is adopted internationally to indicate the degree of protection afforded by an enclosure against solid or liquid materials entering it. The classification is indicated by the letters **IP** followed by two digits; the first of these indicates the degree of protection against entry of solid materials from 0 (no protection) to 6 (complete protection against ingress of dust.) The second digit indicates protection against entry of liquid (0 up to 8, which is protection against indefinite immersion in water under pressure). BS 5490 gives the full details of this system.

Guidance Note PM29 'Electrical hazards from steam/water pressure cleaners' gives comprehensive advice on the protection of electrical equipment in a highly conducting environment.

2.1.6. Summary Of Key Points

- The risk of electrocution can be reduced if live equipment is provided with protection and/or insulation which is both suitable for its intended use and the environment in which it is to be used.

- The Index of Protection provides a measure of the degree of protection against hostile environments offered by particular items of electrical equipment.

- Equipment may be damaged when it is exposed to:

  a) abrasion/impact;

  b) repeated stress;

  c) a hostile environment.

2.1.7. Measures used to protect against electric shock in the event of a system fault.

Relevant Regulations

Regulation 4. Systems, work activities and protective equipment.
Regulation 8. Earthing or other suitable precautions.
Regulation 9. Integrity of referenced conductors.
Regulation 11. Means for protecting from excess of current.
Regulation 13. Precautions for work on equipment made dead.

There are three measures which can be taken to reduce the risk if a fault occurs in a system:

i) design and construct the system so that uninsulated conductors cannot become 'live';

ii) the potential difference involved and the size and duration of the resulting electric current are such that if the conductors do become live no danger will arise;

iii) if the conductors do become charged their environment is such that danger will not arise.

One or more of these measures may be taken in combination to reduce the risk of shock. A number of techniques are used to effect the measures. We will be examining them in greater detail in Modules 3 and 4. For the moment it is sufficient for you to be aware of them and which of the measures listed above they support. The techniques are:

a) **double insulation** - Live parts of the equipment are covered by two separated layers of insulating material. In theory a single layer would be sufficient to provide the protection required. The presence of a second layer provides a back up to the first and removes the need to earth the outer metal casing of the equipment. This method depends upon the insulation remaining intact, so the proper maintenance and use of equipment constructed in this way is essential.

b) **earthing** - The public electricity supply in this country, 240 volts (single phase) a.c. and 415 volts (three phase) a.c. is referenced to earth. This is achieved by making a deliberate connection to earth at the power transformer. This has the advantage of tying the supply voltage to a constant reference point. The neutral line is always at a potential of zero volts at the point where it is tied to earth.

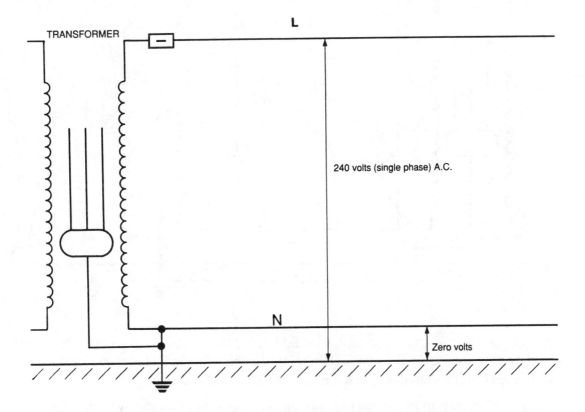

By earthing the exposed metal parts which should not normally carry current, any fault current is provided with a low impedance path to earth.

The current flows along a circular path, the fault loop. It is important that the impedance of the fault loop is very small so that:

i) a large enough fault current flows to operate any protective devices (fuses, residual current devices) so cutting off the current by breaking the circuit;

ii) the human body presents a relatively large impedance and only a very small current flows through anyone touching the exposed metal parts during the brief period between the fault developing and the operation of the protective device.

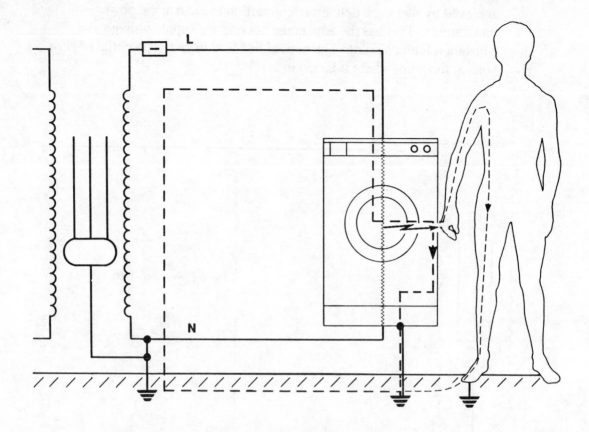

It is important that the earth conductor should be able to withstand any earth fault current which might conceivably flow through it. Nothing should be included in the earth circuit which stops or offers resistance to the flow of an earth fault current.

c) **Connection to a common voltage reference point on the system**. The referencing of the public electricity supply to earth was mentioned in the last section. By referencing the supply in this way, any earth faults on electrical equipment can be detected and the supply to that equipment cut off by the operation of the protective devices.

d) **equipotential bonding** - This protective technique is important in places such as bathrooms where electricity, water, and a variety of metal objects (baths, shower fittings, radiators, taps, water pipes etc.) are brought together in close proximity. The metal fittings are all linked by a common conductor which ensures that all exposed metal is at the same potential. A current will not flow between two points at the same potential, so if any of the metal fittings become live through contact with a live conductor any of the other metal fittings can be touched simultaneously without the risk of electric shock. A common connection with earth is usually made.

e)   **use of safe voltages** - The severity of electric shock increases significantly in highly conducting locations. A degree of protection is provided by the use of low voltages.

As we have already seen 50 volts a.c. or 120 volts d.c. are considered to be 'safe'. This does not mean that precautions such as earthing and bonding can be dispensed with. In surroundings which are wet or which contain a high proportion of metal even these 'safe' voltages can be dangerous.

Building sites provide particularly hazardous environments. Safety can be improved by the use of equipment running off a centre-tapped 110 volt (single phase) a.c. supply.

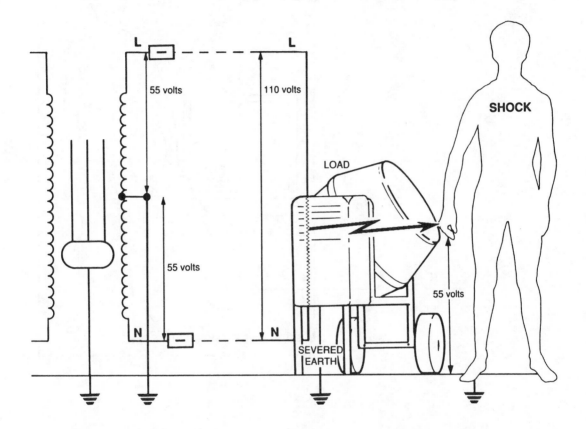

This allows the equipment to be powered by 110 volt supply but the maximum shock voltage to earth is 55 volts in the event of direct contact with a line conductor, e.g. as a result of damage, which exposes the live conductor and severs the protective earth conductor. In the event of direct contact or an earth fault, the maximum potential which can be experienced by anyone in contact with earth, who is unlucky enough to be in contact with a live part, is 55 volts.

Lower voltages which represent even less of a threat should be used in particularly hazardous environments e.g. vehicle washing areas. Guidance Note PM37 'Electrical installations in motor vehicle repair premises', recommends that if electrical equipment is essential, it should preferably operate at 25 volts or less.

f) **Earth-free non-conducting environments**. - If the power supply is earth-referenced, and work is carried out in an earth-free non-conducting area, dangerous potentials to earth are eliminated because no path exists for earth fault currents. Consequently, there is no danger of electric shock. Although an attractive method of protection against electric shock it is difficult to maintain in practice and therefore only has very specialised applications, e.g. TV repair workshops.

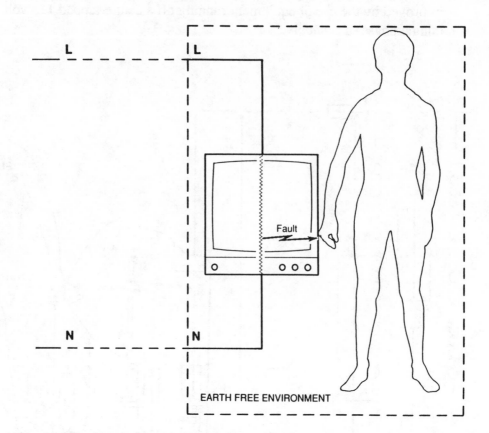

g) **Current Limitation** - Protection against electric shock from direct contact may be achieved by the use of equipment which incorporates a means of limiting the output energy, typically a high source impedance limiting output current. It must be directly applied to the line (phase) conductor and not the neutral conductor. Because of the severe limitation on output energy this technique is not widely used!

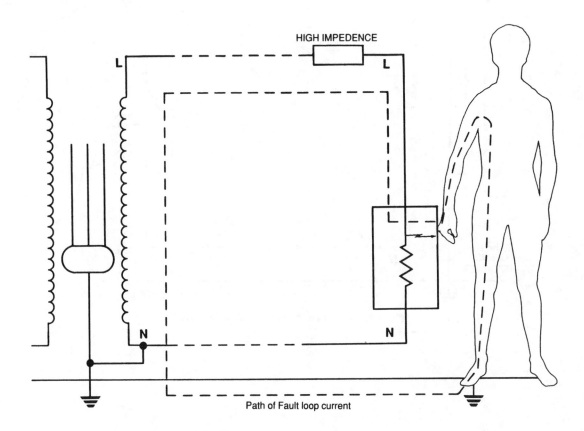

Path of Fault loop current

The fault loop current should not exceed 5mA if this method is to provide adequate protection. Although the shock would not be lethal if it is of short duration it would still be felt. In these circumstances indirect injury may be caused by the victim falling, etc., and is not within the scope of the Electricity at Work regulations.

h) **Separated or Isolated Systems** - The commonest example of this type of protection is the circuit which supplies power for an electric shaver in the bathroom.

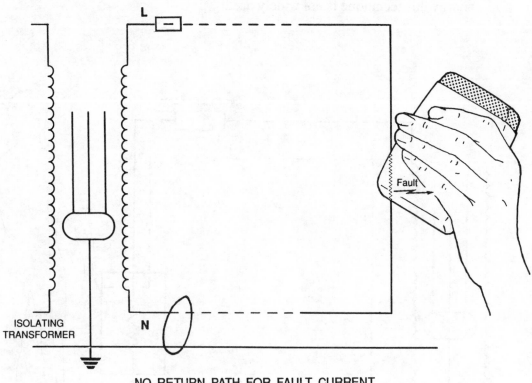

NO RETURN PATH FOR FAULT CURRENT

In this type of system the power source is an isolating transformer with an unearthed secondary. The electrical separation between the earthed core of the transformer and the secondary winding represents a gap in the fault loop which prevents the flow of a fault current. If a fault current cannot flow the danger of electric shock is removed. However, if the system developed a fault which resulted in it being earthed, the danger would return.

Such systems should be regularly checked to ensure that they remain isolated.

That concludes our brief review of the techniques applied to effect one or more of the measures outlined at the beginning of this section. We will now round the section off by relating appropriate techniques to individual measures.

2.1.8. Summary Of Techniques

MEASURE		TECHNIQUE
i)	The system is so designed and constructed that uninsulated conductors cannot become live	• Double insulation
ii)	If the conductors do become 'live', the potential difference involved and the size and duration of the resulting electric current are such that no danger will arise	• earthing • equipotential bonding • use of safe voltages • current limitation • connection to a common voltage reference point on the system
iii)	If the conductors do become charged their environment is such that danger will not arise	• separated or isolated systems • earth-free, non conducting environments

2.1.9. Self Assessment Questions Test

1. SAQ - Index of Protection

Indicate which of the following statements are true and which are false, by drawing a circle around the appropriate letter.

a) Each digit of an IP number represents protection offered against a different hazard. T/F

b) The IP number is a measure of the combined protection offered by a piece of equipment against the entry of solid material and liquids, and ranges from 0 to 99. T/F

c) In an IP number, the larger the digit, the greater the degree of protection. T/F

d) An IP number of 32 indicates greater protection against the entry of water than does one of 18. T/F

2. SAQ - Double Insulation

Tick the option which you think completes the statement correctly.

An electrical device protected by double insulation has

a) a single layer of insulation of double normal thickness. ☐

b) two discrete layers of insulation. ☐

c) insulation on both the live and non-conducting metal components. ☐

d) an isolated power source as well as normal insulation. ☐

3. SAQ - Earthing

Tick the option which you think completes the following statement correctly.

The low impedance path to earth provided when electrical equipment is earthed

a) allows an earth fault current to flow which is of sufficient size to operate protective devices. ☐

b) ensures that no earth fault current will flow through the body of anyone using the equipment if a fault develops. ☐

c) prevents a system overload if any protective devices fail to operate. ☐

d) eliminates any real need for insulation within the equipment. ☐

4. SAQ - Connection to a common voltage reference point on the system

Complete the following statement

Earth faults on electrical equipment can be detected and the supply cut off by the operation of protective devices because the public electricity supply is ...

_____

5. SAQ - Equipotential bonding

Tick the correct response to the following situation.

The metal fittings in a bathroom are protected by equipotential bonding. A wiring fault develops so that the water taps become live. A man using the bathroom is simultaneously touching one of the taps and a steel radiator. What will happen to him?

a) He may experience a slight tingling as a small, high voltage current flows through his body. □

b) He may experience a severe shock but it will be of very short duration. □

c) He will probably be unaware of the current flowing through his body between the two conductors. □

d) He will not experience any sensation because a current will not flow between the two conductors. □

6. SAQ - Use of Safe Voltages

Tick the option which you think completes the following statement correctly.

By centre-tapping a 110 volt transformer

a) 110 volts are supplied to power any equipment but in the event of an earth fault developing the transformer is cut off. □

b) the power is supplied at 55 volts which represents only a minor hazard in the event of an earth fault developing. □

c) the power is supplied at 55 volts and the maximum potential an operative can be exposed to is 55 volts. □

d) the supply to any equipment is maintained at 110 volts but in the event of an earth fault developing an operative can only be exposed to a potential of 55 volts. □

7. SAQ - Current Limitation

Complete the following statement:

The protective technique of current limitation is not widely used because of...

_____

1. Response - SAQ - Index of Protection

Indicate which of the following statements are true and which are false, by drawing a circle around the appropriate letter.

a)   Each digit of an IP number represents protection offered against
       a different hazard   Ⓣ F

This statement is true. The first digit indicates the degree of protection against entry of solid materials and ranges from 0 to 6. The second indicates protection against the entry of liquids and ranges from 0 to 8.

b)   The IP number is a measure of the combined protection offered
       by a piece of equipment against the entry of solid material
       and liquids, and ranges from 0 to 99.   T Ⓕ

This statement is false.

c)   In an IP number, the larger the digit, the greater the degree
       of protection.   Ⓣ F

The statement is true. The greatest protection offered against the ingress of solid material is indicated by the number 6; the greatest protection against the entry of a liquid by 8.

d)   An IP number of 32 indicates greater protection against
       the entry of water than does one of 18.   T Ⓕ

This statement is false. The second digit is a measure of the protection offered against liquids. 8 is the highest protection against liquids.

2. Response - SAQ - Double Insulation

Tick the option which you think completes the statement correctly.

An electrical device protected by double insulation has

a)   a single layer of insulation of double normal thickness.   ☐

b)   two discrete layers of insulation.   ✓

c)   insulation on both the live and non-conducting metal
       components.   ☐

d)   an isolated power source as well as normal insulation.   ☐

The correct option is (b).

An electrical device protected by double insulation has two discrete layers of insulation.

3. Response - SAQ - Earthing

The correct option is (a).

The low impedance path to earth provided when electrical equipment is earthed allows an earth fault current to flow which is of sufficient size to operate protective devices.

    (b)   is incorrect. An earth fault current would flow through the body of anyone who touched the exposed metal of an electrical device that had developed an earth fault. However, if the earth conductor has a very low impedance, the current flowing through the body would be very small. In addition, if the protection device operates correctly, then current flow would be of short duration.

    (c)   is incorrect. If any protective device failed to operate large fault currents would flow because the electrical resistance of its path to earth is low.

    (d)   is incorrect. Insulation or some sort of protection is necessary to guard against short circuits.

4. Response - SAQ - Connection to a common voltage reference point on the system

Earth faults on electrical equipment can be detected and the supply cut off by the operation of protective devices because the public electricity supply is **referenced to earth.**

5. Response - SAQ -Equipotential bonding

Tick the correct response to the following situation.

The metal fittings in a bathroom are protected by equipotential bonding. A wiring fault develops so that the water taps become live. A man using the bathroom is simultaneously touching one of the taps and a steel radiator. What will happen to him?

    a)   He may experience a slight tingling as a small, high voltage current flows through his body. ☐

    b)   He may experience a severe shock but it will be of very short duration. ☐

    c)   He will probably be unaware of the current flowing through his body between the two conductors. ☐

    d)   He will not experience any sensation because a current will not flow between the two conductors. ✓

The correct response is (d). He will be unaware that the tap is live because no current will flow through his body between the two conductors. They will both be at the same potential and an electric current will not flow between two points on a conductor which are at the same potential.

6. Response - SAQ - Use of Safe Voltages

Tick the option which you think completes the following statement correctly.

By centre-tapping a 110 volt transformer

a) 110 volts are supplied to power any equipment but in the event of an earth fault developing the transformer is cut off. ☐

b) the power is supplied at 55 volts which represents only a minor hazard in the event of an earth fault developing. ☐

c) the power is supplied at 55 volts and the maximum potential an operative can be exposed to is 55 volts. ☐

d) the supply to any equipment is maintained at 110 volts but in the event of an earth fault developing an operative can only be exposed to a potential of 55 volts. ☑

The correct option is (d). By centre tapping a 110 volt transformer the supply to any equipment is maintained at 110 volts. In the event of an earth fault developing, an operative can only be exposed to a potential of 55 volts.

7. Response - SAQ - Current Limitation

The protective technique of current limitation is not widely used because of **the limitation on output energy.**

2.1.10. Electric Burn

2.1.10.1. Circumstances in which the risk of electric burn may arise

As we saw in Module 1 electric burns are one of the injuries inflicted by an electric current as it passes through the body. The greatest amount of energy is dissipated where resistance to the flow of current is highest. This usually occurs on the surface of the body within the skin layer at the points where the current enters and leaves the body. However, internal burning, deep within the body, can result from the passage of a large electric current. Internal burns can prove fatal.

2.1.10.2. Measures used to protect against electric burn

The circumstances which give rise to the risk of electric shock similarly create the risk of electric burn. The measures which reduce the risk of shock also provide protection against the risk of electric burn.

2.1.11. Electric Arcing

2.1.11.1. Circumstances when arcing can occur

We explained why arcing occurs in Module 1. For an arc to be formed there must be sufficient electrical energy to maintain a conductive path across a space which has, initially at least, a very high resistance between two conductors. Although this implies the presence of large electrical potentials this is not necessarily the case. Arcs can be generated by relatively low voltage, but high energy, power sources. The arc which forms when a car battery is shorted to the car body is a good example.

Once an arc forms it creates its own conductive path by ionising the air in the widening gap. The higher the voltage of the power source, the wider the gap which the arc can cross.

It is often necessary for electricians to test for the presence of a voltage or to measure voltages in electrical systems. Burns due to arcing account for a number of serious accidents during electrical testing each year.

2.1.11.2. Measures taken to reduce the risk of arcing

An arc may be struck when a conductor

    i)   is brought near an exposed live conductor carrying a high voltage;

    or

    ii)   touches, and then is drawn away from a live conductor carrying a low voltage.

In addition an arc may be struck across the gap which is created when a live conductor is broken, (e.g. arcing at a switch). An arc cannot be struck between adequately insulated conductors.

Consequently the risk can be reduced by:

i)   ensuring that live conductors are insulated or protected so that contact cannot be
       made

       or, if making contact is unavoidable,

ii)   limiting the amount of exposed metal which is brought into contact with the
       live conductor.

In the example given above of the danger of arcing during testing, the risk can be
significantly reduced by using properly designed equipment.

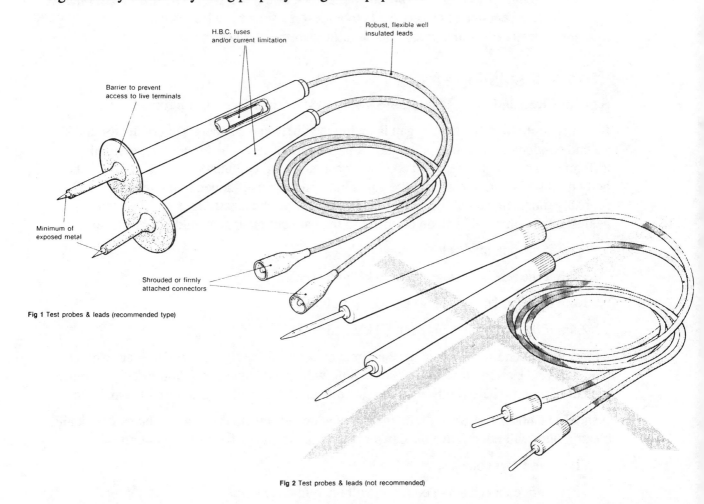

Fig 1 Test probes & leads (recommended type)

Fig 2 Test probes & leads (not recommended)

The illustration shown above is taken from Guidance Note GS 38 'Electrical test equipment
for use by technicians'. The Guidance Note suggests that the test probes and leads used in
conjunction with equipment used to test for or measure voltages, should have the following
features:

a) The probes should:

i)   have finger barriers or be shaped so as to guard against inadvertent hand contact
       with the live conductors under test;

ii)   be insulated so as to leave an exposed metal tip not exceeding 2mm measured
       across any surface of the tip. Where practicable it is strongly recommended
       that this be reduced to 1mm or less, or that spring loaded screened probes be
       used.

b) The leads should:

    i)   be adequately insulated (choice of insulating material may be influenced by the environment in which the leads are to be used);

    ii)   be coloured, so that one lead can be readily distinguished from the other;

    iii)   be flexible and sufficiently robust for the duty expected of them;

    iv)   be long enough for the purpose, while not overlong so as to be clumsy or unwieldly;

    v)   not have accessible exposed conductors, other than the probe tips, nor should live conductors be accessible to a person's finger if a lead becomes detached from a probe, indicator or instrument when in use.

2.1.11.3. Insulating air gaps

Relevant Regulations: Regulation 14 Work on or near live conductors.

If a sufficiently wide insulating gap is maintained between an energised conductor and a second conductor at a lower potential, arcing cannot occur. The higher the potential difference between an energised conductor and a second conductor, (which could be the body of a workman), the greater the gap which must be maintained to prevent arcing. This is probably most relevant to the uninsulated overhead public electricity supply system. The nearest approach of any person or object to the bare conductors should not be closer than:

    0.8m if the potential is less than 20 kV;

    1.0m if the potential is between 20 kV and 40 kV;

    1.4m if the potential is between 40 kV and 80 kV;

    2.4m if the potential is between 80 kV and 160 kV.

Atmospheric conditions would have a direct effect on these figures. A damp atmosphere would have the effect of reducing them. Safe working distances would normally be much greater than those listed above to allow for movement, tools being held in the hand, etc.

It should be noted that some of the measures which eliminate the risk of electric shock and electric burn will not remove the danger of arcing. It may still occur in systems which:

    i)   use low voltages;

    ii)   are connected to a common voltage reference point;

    iii)   are earthed;

    iv)   are separated or isolated;

    v)   make use of equipotential bonding.

2.1.12. Explosions

Relevant Regulations:
Regulation 4 . Systems, work activities and protective equipment
Regulation 5. Strength and capability of electrical equipment
Regulation 6. Adverse or hazardous environments

2.1.12.1. Circumstances where explosions might occur.

As we saw in Module 1, explosions related to electrical systems can be assigned to either of two categories.

(i)   Those involving the violent disintegration of electrical equipment either as a result of an excessively high current being passed through or after prolonged internal arcing.

(ii)   Those which result from the ignition of a flammable gas, vapour or dust by an electric spark or arc.

Explosions in the first category are related and can only be the result of the passage of large currents, whilst those in the second can result from the flow of very small currents.

Switch gear, motors and power cables are liable to suffer an electrical explosion if they are misused. On the other hand, explosions resulting from an electrical spark or arc can occur wherever flammable gases, vapours and dusts are present.

2.1.12.2. Measures taken to reduce the risk of explosion

The electrical explosion of a piece of equipment can be prevented by the use of any protective device which limits the electric current/energy flowing through it. Failure to provide electrical equipment of sufficient 'strength and capability' as required by Regulation 5 or failure to construct and maintain an electrical system 'so as to prevent danger' as required by Regulation 4 can give rise to a risk of electrical explosion.

Preventing the ignition of a flammable substance by an electric spark or arc is much more difficult. The smallest spark can be sufficient to trigger an explosion and much care must be given to the design of electrical equipment used in flammable atmospheres.

Regulation 6 requires that any electrical equipment *'foreseeably exposed to any flammable or explosive substance ..... shall be of such construction or as necessary protected ..... to prevent ..... any danger arising.'*

2.1.13. Fire

2.1.13.1. Circumstances where fire may occur

Fire can result wherever there is:

a) electrical sparking or arcing;
b) a flammable substance close to or touching electrically heated surfaces.

2.1.13.2. Measures to reduce the risk of fire

The proper installation of electrical conductors and the regular maintenance of electrical equipment will reduce the risk of fire both from arcing and overheated conductors. The removal of flammable substances from contact with electrically heated surfaces will further reduce the risk. Electrical equipment or conductors which could get hot in fault conditions should not be positioned next to flammable substances e.g. cables should not be run under carpets.

2.1.14. Self Assessment Question Test

1. SAQ - Accidents associated with electrical testing.

Complete the following statement by ticking the appropriate option.

It is often necessary for electricians to test for the presence of a voltage or to measure voltages in electrical systems. In these circumstances the majority of accidents involve:

a)   electric shock; ☐

b)   electric arcing; ☐

c)   electric explosion; ☐

d)   fire or explosion initiated by electricity. ☐

2. SAQ - Arcing

Indicate whether the following statements are true or false by circling the appropriate letter.

a)   The measures used to eliminate the risk of electric shock and burn will
      eliminate the risk of arcing.   T/F

b)   Arcing may occur in systems which use low voltages.   T/F

c)   Arcing cannot occur in systems which are earthed.   T/F

d)   Arcing may occur in systems which make use of equipotential bonding.   T/F

1. Response - SAQ - Accidents associated with electrical testing.

Complete the following statement by ticking the appropriate option.

It is often necessary for electricians to test for the presence of a voltage or to measure voltages in electrical systems. In these circumstances the majority of accidents involve:

a) electric shock; ☐

b) electric arcing; ☑

c) electric explosion; ☐

d) fire or explosion initiated by electricity. ☐

The correct option is (b). When electricians test for the presence of a voltage or measure the voltages in electrical systems, the majority of accidents involve electric arcing.

2. Response - SAQ - Arcing

Indicate whether the following statements are true or false by circling the appropriate letter.

a) The measures used to eliminate the risk of electric shock and burn will eliminate the risk of arcing.   T/Ⓕ

This statement is FALSE. The measures which eliminate the risk of electric shock and burn will not remove the risk of arcing.

b) Arcing may occur in systems which use low voltages.   Ⓣ/F

This statement is TRUE. An arc can be struck between two conductors where the potential difference between them is only a few volts, providing that there is sufficient energy present.

c) Arcing cannot occur in systems which are earthed.   T/Ⓕ

This statement is FALSE. An arc can be struck between a conductor which is at earth potential and one which is at a higher potential, provided there is sufficient electrical energy present.

d) Arcing may occur in systems which make use of equipotential bonding.   Ⓣ/F

This statement is TRUE. An arc can be struck between a live conductor and a second which is equipotentially bonded. There is a chance of this occurring so long as there is a potential difference betwen the live conductor and the bonded conductor and there is sufficient electrical energy available.

2.1.15. Summary of Key Points

- Electric burns are inflicted when an electric current flows through the body.

- The measures which are taken to eliminate the risk of electric shock will also eliminate the risk of electric burn but they will not eliminate the risk of arcing.

- Electric arcs can be generated by relatively low voltage power sources provided sufficient energy is available.

- Burns due to arcing account for more accidents in electrical testing than are caused by electric shocks.

- The risk of arcing can be reduced by ensuring contact cannot be made between conductors or, if this is not possible, limiting the amount of exposed metal which is brought into contact with the live conductor.

- Electrical explosions which result in the violent disintegration of electrical equipment result from the passage of an excessively high current or prolonged internal arcing.

- Electrically induced fires and explosions can result from a single electric spark.

2.1.16. End Test

1. Does the victim of electric shock always have to be in contact with a live conductor? Explain your answer.

2. Why is someone standing on the ground not necessarily at the same potential as the earth?

3. What are the highest d.c. and a.c. voltages which are assumed to be normally safe?

4. How can conductors be protected against impact/abrasion damage?

5. Why should electric cables be kept out of contact with oil and petrol?

6. What power source should be used in place of electricity in highly conducting environments?

7. You wish to use an electric drill in a very damp, hence highly conducting environment. You have a choice of two. The first has an IP number of 56, the second an IP number of 48. Explain your choice.

8. It is decided to use equipotential bonding as a protective measure in a workshop. What would this entail?

9. Why would an increase in the electrical resistance of an earth conductor be potentially dangerous?

10. The measures taken to eliminate electric shock may not be sufficient to prevent the danger of arcing. Why does the danger remain?

End Test - Answers

1. Does the victim of electric shock always have to be in contact with a live conductor? Explain your answer.

No. If the potential difference between an uninsulated live conductor and a person standing close to it is sufficiently large enough there is a risk of electrocution. In these circumstances the electric current might 'leap' the gap between the conductor and the victim's body.

The narrower the gap between the two, the greater the risk.

2. Why is someone standing on the ground not necessarily at the same potential as the earth?

In order to be at the same potential as the earth, anyone standing on it would also have to be in good electrical contact with it. There are a number of factors which might prevent this, such as the nature of the ground, the type of footwear being worn, etc.

3. What are the highest d.c. and a.c. voltages which are assumed to be normally safe?

The highest d.c. and a.c. voltages internationally accepted as safe are 110 volts and 50 volts respectively. However, in highly conducting environments where it is very damp, and/or there is a high proportion of metal present even these 'safe' potentials might be dangerous.

4. How can conductors be protected against impact/abrasion damage?

Any of the following measures may be used to prevent impact/abrasion damage.

(i) Enclose the cable within a protective cover, e.g. a metal conduit.

(ii) Bury the cable below ground, or raise it above ground to a sufficiently safe height.

(iii) Use armoured cable which is capable of withstanding any forseeable impact or abrasion.

5. Why should electric cables be kept out of contact with oil and petrol?

Oil and petrol can damage the electrical insulation on the cable. The conductor it protects may become exposed and give rise to danger.

6. What power source should be used in place of electricity in highly conducting environments?

Where possible, compressed air should be used to drive hand-held power tools in highly conducting environments.

7. You wish to use an electric drill in a very damp, hence highly conducting environment. You have a choice of two. The first has an IP number of 56, the second an IP number of 48. Explain your choice.

The second drill should be chosen. The second digit is a measure of the equipment's resistance to the entry of water and other liquids, and can have a value from 0 to 8. An IP number of 48 indicates that the drill is completely protected against water.

8. It is decided to use equipotential bonding as a protective measure in a workshop. What would this entail?

All the exposed metal items in the workshop e.g. pipes, radiators, rails etc., would be linked by conductors. The resulting network would then be earthed.

Should a fault occur the risk of being simultaneously in contact with two conductors at different potentials would be significantly reduced.

9. Why would an increase in the electrical resistance of an earth conductor be potentially dangerous?

An increase in the electrical resistance of an earth conductor may be potentially dangerous because of the effect this might have on the current which would flow to earth if a fault occurred. A high resistance might reduce the fault current to the level where it would fail to operate any protective device incorporated into the faulty circuit.

10. The measures taken to eliminate electric shock may not be sufficient to prevent the danger of arcing. Why does the danger remain?

The danger remains because arcs can be created by low voltage currents which are too low to produce an electric shock. If the conductor carrying the current is touched against a second conductor, at a lower potential and then drawn away, an arc is formed across the air gap between the two.

MODULE THREE

CONTENTS

Introduction

This module covers Regulations 4 to 12.

Regulation 4 is general in its application. It lays down, in very broad terms, what must be done to make work on or near electrical systems safe. Specific requirements are set out in Regulations 5 to 16. A consideration of Regulations 5 to 12 forms the bulk of this module. These Regulations set out what is required of the hardware of electrical systems to ensure the safety of those working on or near them. Regulations 13 to 16 focus on working practices and these are dealt with in the fourth and final module.

Module 3 is made up of five units; they are not of equal length. Unit 1 which is concerned with Regulation 4, 'Systems, work activities and protective equipment' stands alone because of its general nature.

There is an association between the strength of equipment and the environment in which it is used and so Regulation 5, 'Strength and capability of electrical equipment', and Regulation 6, 'Adverse or hazardous environments,' are linked in Unit 2.

Regulation 7, 'Insulation, protection and placing of conductors', complements Regulation 10, 'Connections', so together they form the subject matter of Unit 3.

Similar reasoning lies behind the choice of the Regulations discussed in Unit 4, that is Regulation 8, 'Earthing and other suitable precautions', and Regulation 9, 'Integrity of referenced conductors.'

In the fifth and last unit of this module we consider the implications of Regulations 11 and 12. The former is concerned with the need to prevent danger arising from an excess of current, while the latter sets out what is required of the means used to cut off power and to effect the electrical isolation of equipment.

UNIT 1

3.1.1. Aim

The aim of this unit is to familiarise you with the content and implications of Regulation 4.

Objectives

When you have worked through this unit you will be able to:

- explain the meaning of the word 'constructed' as it is used in Regulation 4(1);
- list the factors which should be taken into account when assessing the suitability of the construction of electrical systems to prevent danger;
- state when there is an obligation to maintain equipment;
- explain what duty holders should do to be certain that a maintenance programme meets the maintenance requirement;
- outline the general safety precautions which should be taken when work is carried out in association with electrical systems;
- explain what should be done with electrical equipment when it is decommissioned or abandoned;
- explain the implications of Regulation 4(4).

3.1.2. Overview

Regulation 4 is very general, and hence very wide in its application. The link between this general Regulation and the specific requirements of safety, set out in the Regulations which follow, is demonstrated at the start of the unit.

After this introduction each of the four sections of the Regulation are considered in turn and the points raised developed so that the intention of the Regulation is clarified.

3.1.3. Regulation 4: Systems, work activities and protective equipment

4(1). All systems shall at all times be of such construction as to prevent, so far as is reasonably practicable, danger.

4(2). As may be necessary to prevent danger, all systems shall be maintained so as to prevent, so far as is reasonably practicable, such danger.

4(3). Every work activity, including operation, use and maintenance of a system and work near a system, shall be carried out in such a manner as not to give rise, so far as is reasonably practicable, to danger.

4(4). Any equipment provided under these Regulations for the purpose of protecting persons at work on or near electrical equipment shall be suitable for the use for which it is provided, be maintained in a condition suitable for that use, and be properly used.

Related Regulations

Regulation 4 is supported by the requirements set out in the other Regulations.

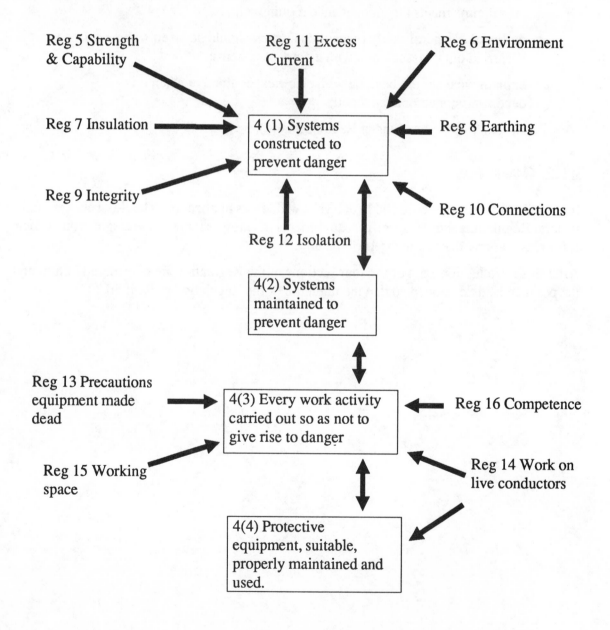

3.1.3.1. Regulation 4(1)

All systems shall at all times be of such construction as to prevent, so far as is reasonably practicable, danger.

What is meant by the construction of a system?

We have already seen that systems can extend over large areas and be extremely complex. When the Regulation refers to the "construction of a system" this term covers:

- the design of the system;
- the design of its component parts;
- the arrangement and assembly of those parts;
- their physical condition.

Each of these elements would have to be considered separately and together when assessing the suitability of the construction of the system to prevent danger.

Time Factor

The time factor indicated in this clause is important. The construction should be such that danger from any likely or foreseeable circumstance should be prevented at any time during the life of the system. This requirement holds not only while the system is in operation, but also during any testing, commissioning and maintenance. Moreover, circuits for testing and commissioning must also comply with this Regulation.

Factors influencing the construction of a system to prevent danger.

There are a number of factors which must be taken into consideration when considering how the system should be constructed. These are:

1. how it is to be set up and maintained;
2. how it is to be used;
3. where it is to be used;
4. what work it will be required to do;
5. what faults may develop in the system and in any attached system;
6. what protection will be needed.

Care should to be taken in the selection of equipment so that it fulfils the anticipated requirements.

The safety of a system depends, among other things, upon:

1. proper selection of electrical equipment,
2. proper consideration of inter-relationships between items of equipment.

3.1.3.2. Regulation 4(2)

As may be necessary to prevent danger, all systems shall be maintained so as to prevent, so far as is reasonably practicable, such danger.

The requirement to maintain equipment is only applicable if failure to do so would result in danger. The frequency of maintenance inspections and the quality of the work carried out is at the discretion of the duty holders. They should base any decision on experience and on the appraisal of all available relevant information, eg. equipment manufacturers' guidance. Even then, they cannot be certain or demonstrate they are meeting the maintenance requirements unless they keep accurate records of all the maintenance work undertaken.

Maintenance

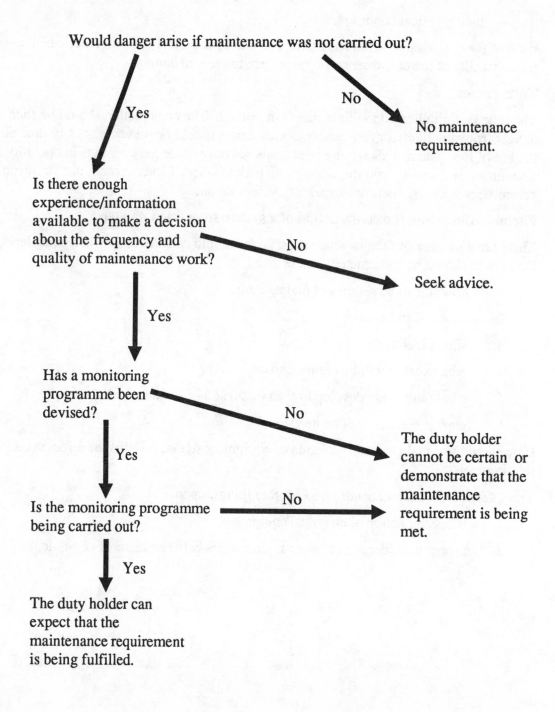

Would danger arise if maintenance was not carried out?

Yes

No

No maintenance requirement.

Is there enough experience/information available to make a decision about the frequency and quality of maintenance work?

No

Seek advice.

Yes

Has a monitoring programme been devised?

No

Yes

The duty holder cannot be certain or demonstrate that the maintenance requirement is being met.

Is the monitoring programme being carried out?

No

Yes

The duty holder can expect that the maintenance requirement is being fulfilled.

90

3.1.3.3. Regulation 4(3)

Every work activity including operation, use and maintenance of a system and work near a system, shall be carried out in such a manner as not to give rise, so far as is reasonably practicable, to danger.

This clause refers to work directly or indirectly associated with an electrical system. The work may be carried out on or near such a system and need not necessarily be of an electrical nature.

General Safety Measures

For work of an electrical nature there is a recognised sequence of steps which should be followed to ensure safety.

The sequence is as follows.

1. Clearly identify the work to be done.

2. Plan the work to include safety measures, selection of people, supervision, etc.

3. Wherever possible make the equipment dead before the work starts.

4. Isolate and secure (lock-off) the equipment so that it cannot be inadvertently re-charged or re-energised.

5. Prove any test instrument to be used to confirm that the equipment is dead before the test is carried out.

6. Use the test instrument to prove the equipment is dead at the point of work before work commences.

7. Prove the test instrument again to confirm that it is still working.

Each operation should be carried out by people properly qualified to do the work and the whole process should be controlled by proper safe systems of work. This will be discussed later in the course when Regulations 12 and 13 are reviewed.

Disused electrical equipment/systems

Equipment which has been decommissioned or abandoned can be a source of danger. The following procedure should be followed to ensure that danger does not arise.

1. Before the equipment is abandoned or decommissioned it should be disconnected from all sources of electricity and isolated. This includes making the disconnection secure.

2. Equipment abandoned or decommissioned should preferably be removed, or if this is not practicable, once it has been established that the equipment is dead and cannot be re-charged or re-energised, a notice should be attached to it to ensure that it remains so.

3.1.3.4. Regulation 4(4)

Any equipment provided under these Regulations for the purpose of protecting persons at work on or near electrical equipment shall be suitable for the use for which it is provided, be maintained in a condition suitable for that use, and be properly used.

The defence outlined in Regulation 29 is available in any proceedings for an offence under this part of Regulation 4.

Protective Equipment

This Regulation is not qualified by the phrase "so far as is reasonably practicable" and no reference is made to danger or injury. So, wherever the Regulations stipulate the provision of protective equipment this duty is absolute, and the equipment must conform with the requirement of 4(4). This requires that it should be suitable for the use for which it is provided and that it should be properly maintained as well as properly used.

Employees have an absolute duty to use protective equipment which has been provided for their use.

To complete Unit 1 we would now like you to attempt the self- assessment questions which follow.

3.1.4. Self Assessment Question Test

1. SAQ - Construction

'All systems shall at all times be of such construction as to prevent, so far as is reasonably practicable, danger.'

In the list below tick the items which the word 'construction' may be considered to cover.

a)   The design of the system.   ☐

b)   The design of the system's components.   ☐

c)   The arrangements of the components.   ☐

d)   The physical condition of the components.   ☐

Tick the option which completes the following statement correctly.

The appraisal of the suitability of the system's construction:

a)   is carried out only when the system is first assembled.   ☐

b)   can take place at any time during its life.   ☐

2. SAQ - Assessing the suitability of a system's construction

In the space below list FOUR of the factors which should be taken into account when assessing the suitability of a system's construction to prevent danger.

1._____

2._____

3._____

4._____

3. SAQ - Maintenance

Indicate which of the following statements are true or false by ringing the appropriate letter.

a)   Regulation 4 imposes a duty to maintain equipment/systems only where people are employed on or near them.   T/F

b)   All equipment/systems shall be maintained so that, so far as it is reasonably practicable, danger is prevented.   T/F

c)   Regulation 4 imposes a duty to maintain systems only if danger would otherwise result.   T/F

d)   If danger can be prevented by maintenance, the frequency of such a programme is left to the discretion of the duty holder.   T/F

e)   If danger can be prevented by maintenance, the quality of the maintenance work carried out is left to the discretion of the duty holder.   T/F

4. SAQ - Meeting the maintenance requirement

Tick the option which correctly completes the following statement.

A duty holder can only be certain that a maintenance programme is meeting the requirements of the Regulation if

a)   no accidents have occurred.   ☐

b)   the programme is monitored.   ☐

c)   those entrusted with the work are of proven competence.   ☐

d)   the system is properly constructed so as to prevent danger.   ☐

5. SAQ- General safety precautions

The general safety precautions which should be taken when work is carried out on or near an electrical system include the following steps. They are not arranged in the correct sequence.

1.   Conductors proved dead at the point of work.

2.   Conductors securely isolated.

3.   Conductors made dead.

4.   Prove test instrument.

Now arrange the steps in their correct sequence by placing the number set against each step in the appropriate space below. There are four steps and five spaces so one of the steps will have to be repeated.

_____

_____

_____

_____

_____

6. SAQ - Decommissioned or abandoned electrical equipment

a)   What must be done before electrical equipment is decommissioned or abandoned? Write your answer in the space below.

_____

_____

_____

b)   What extra precaution should be taken once the work outlined in (a) has been complete. Use the space below for your answer.

_____

_____

_____

7. SAQ - Regulation 4(4)

Regulation 4(4) requires that equipment provided for the protection of anyone working on or near electrical equipment should be suitable for use, maintained in a suitable condition and properly used.

Circle the correct answer to each of the following questions:

1. Does this requirement hold in all circumstances, whether danger is present or not?   Y/N

2. Is this a requirement only if danger is present?   Y/N

3. Is the equipment provided, maintained and used only so far as it is practicable to do so?   Y/N

The answers to these questions begin on the next page.

1. Response - SAQ - Construction

All systems shall at all times be of such construction as to prevent, so far as is reasonably practicable, danger.

In the list below tick the items the word "construction" maybe considered to cover.

a)   the design of the system   ☑

b)   the design of the system's components   ☑

c)   the arrangement of the components   ☑

d)   the physical condition of the component.   ☑

The appraisal of the suitability of the system's construction

a)   is carried out only when the system is first assembled   ☐

b)   can take place at any time during its life   ☑

2. Response - SAQ - Assessing the suitability of a system's construction

Your list should include any four of the following:

- the manufacturer's assigned or other certified rating of the equipment;

- the likely load and fault conditions;

- the need for suitable electrical protective devices;

- the fault level at the point of supply and the ability of the equipment and the protective devices to handle likely fault conditions;

- any contribution to the fault level from the connected loads such as from motors;

- the environmental conditions which will have a bearing on the mechanical strength and protection required of the equipment;

- the users requirements of the installation;

- the manner in which commissioning, testing and subsequent maintenance or other work may need to be carried out.

3. Response - SAQ - Maintenance

Indicate which of the following statements are true or false by ringing the appropriate letter.

    a)   Regulation 4 imposes a duty to maintain equipment/systems only where
           people are employed on or near them   T (F)

This statement is false. There is an obligation to maintain systems/equipment only if danger could arise from a failure to do so. This could be danger to the public.

    b)   All equipment/systems should be maintained so that so far as it is
           reasonably practicable danger is prevented.   (T)F

This statement is true.

    c)   Regulation 4 imposes a duty to maintain systems only if danger
           would otherwise result.   (T)F

This statement is true.

    d)   If danger can be prevented by maintenance the frequency of such a
           programme is left to the discretion of the duty holder.   (T)F

This statement is true.

    e)   If danger can be prevented by maintenance the quality of the maintenance
           work carried out is left to the discretion of the duty holder.   (T)F

This statement is true.

4. Response - SAQ - Meeting the maintenance requirement

A duty holder can only be certain that a maintenance programme is meeting the requirements of the Regulation if:

    a) no accidents have occurred;   ☐

    b) the programme is monitored;   ☑

    c) those entrusted with the work are of proven competence;   ☐

    d) the system is properly constructed so as to prevent danger. ☐

The correct option is (b). A duty holder can only be certain that a maintenance programme is meeting the requirements of the Regulation if the programme is monitored.

(a), (c) and (d) are wrong. The absence of accidents, the proven competence of the maintenance staff and the knowledge that a system has been properly constructed is no guarantee that the maintenance requirement is being met.

5. Response - SAQ - General safety precaution

The general safety precautions which should be taken when work is carried out on or near an electrical system includes the following steps. They are not arranged in the correct sequence.

1. Conductors proved dead at the point of work.

2. Conductors securely isolated.

3. Conductors made dead.

4. Prove test instrument.

Now arrange the steps in their correct sequence by placing the number set against each step in the appropriate space below. There are four steps and five spaces so one of the steps will have to be repeated twice.

The correct sequence is:

3. Conductors made dead.

2. Conductors securely isolated.

4. Prove test instrument.

1. Conductors proved dead.

4. Prove test instrument.

6. Response - SAQ - Decommissioned or abandoned electrical equipment

a) What must be done before electrical equipment is decommissioned or abandoned? Write your answer in the space below.

It must be disconnected from all sources of supply and isolated. This entails ensuring not only that it is dead but also that it cannot become inadvertently re-energised or charged.

b) What extra precaution should be taken once the work outlined in (a) has been completed. Use the space below for your answer.

Remove it or, if this is not possible, a notice or label clearly indicating that the equipment has been abandoned/decommissioned, should be attached to it. The label should warn against re-energising or re-charging the equipment.

7. Response - SAQ -Regulation 4(4)

Regulation 4(4) requires that equipment provided for the protection of anyone working on or near electrical equipment should be suitable for use, maintained in a suitable condition and properly used.

Circle the correct answer to each of the following questions.

1. Does this requirement hold in all circumstances, whether danger is present or not? (Y)N

2. Is this requirement only if danger is present? Y(N)

The Regulation refers neither to injury nor the risk of injury. Where protective equipment is provided to meet the requirements of the Regulations it must conform to the requirements of 4(4).

3. Is the equipment provided, maintained and used only so far as it is practicable to do so? Y(N)

Regulation 4(4) is not qualified by 'so far as is reasonably practicable'. Where there is a duty to provide protective equipment it is absolute.

3.1.5. Summary Of Key Points

- The word 'construction', when applied to a system, encompasses the design and layout of the system and the design and physical condition of its components.

- The construction of a system should be suitable to prevent danger at all times.

- The obligation to maintain arises only if it would be dangerous not to do so.

- Maintenance records should be kept so that the duty holder can expect that the maintenance requirement is being met.

- Anyone carrying out electrical work should be competent to do so.

- Equipment should preferably be made dead before any work is done on it, and a safe procedure should be followed to achieve this.

- Disused equipment should be isolated, made dead and removed or labelled so that it is not inadvertently re-charged or re-energised.

- The duty to provide and use the protective equipment required by the Regulations is absolute.

UNIT 2

3.2.1. Aim:

The aim of this unit is to familiarise you with the requirements of Regulations 5 and 6.

Objectives

When you have worked through this unit you will be able to:

- explain what is meant by the words 'strength' and 'capability' as they are used in Regulation 5;

- explain the difference between strength, capability and rating;

- explain the importance of taking fault conditions into account when appraising the strength and capability of equipment;

- list the environmental effects Regulation 6 is intended to control;

- give examples of the hazards which electrical equipment may be exposed to, together with the measures which should be taken to counter them.

3.2.2. Overview

This unit is concerned with the requirements set out in Regulations 5 and 6 for electrical equipment to withstand both internal electric stress and external physical attack. It is arranged in two parts which are complementary. The first focuses on the requirement that electrical equipment should have the strength and capability to cope with the electrical stress it may be subjected to during the course of its working life.

The need to operate safely in hazardous environments is the subject of the second part. The nature of the hazards which may be encountered and the protective measures which might be adopted are outlined in this section which concludes with a self assessment question exercise.

3.2.3. Regulation 5: Strength and Capability of Electrical Equipment

No electrical equipment shall be put into use where its strength and capability may be exceeded in such a way as may give rise to danger.

The defence outlined in Regulation 29 is available in any proceedings for an alleged breach of this Regulation.

3.2.3.1. Essential Precautions

The Regulation requires that before a piece of equipment is connected to a system and energised the characteristics of the equipment and the system must be taken into account. This would include an awareness of performance under fault and transient conditions as well as under normal conditions. The purpose is to ensure that when the system is energised the equipment can cope with any voltage stress, heating or electro-magnetic effects safely.

The ability of equipment to withstand the stress generated when a fault develops is particularly important when considering safety. When assessing the suitability of equipment to prevent danger its fault level and the characteristics of any electrical protection should be taken into account. **Remember: the fault level increases as the distance between the power source and the equipment is reduced.**

Most electrical equipment will only withstand short circuit currents for brief periods so any protective devices employed should be capable of clearing faults well within this period.

It is particularly important that protective conductors and equipment should be able to survive beyond fault clearance times.

Requirements of Regulation 5	The Regulation requires that electrical equipment should be capable of withstanding any electrical stress it may be subjected to during its working life.
Equipment/System Characteristics	**How can I ensure that the equipment will comply with this requirement?** Its characteristics under NORMAL, TRANSIENT and FAULT conditions must be matched with those of the system under similar conditions. **What will the equipment be expected to cope with in these different conditions?** It should be able to cope with any electrically-induced stress which might give rise to danger. The effects to be considered include voltage stress and the heating and electro-magnetic effects of the current.
General Application	**Does it apply to all electrical equipment?** Yes, including those items provided solely for protective purposes, e.g. protective conductors.

Fault Conditions	**Why is protective equipment highlighted in that answer?** If such equipment failed in fault conditions before the fault could be cleared a very dangerous situation might easily arise. If equipment is to remain safe in these conditions, fault levels and the characteristics of the excess of current protection, must be taken into account. MOST ELECTRICAL EQUIPMENT WILL ONLY WITHSTAND SHORT CIRCUIT CURRENTS FOR VERY SHORT PERIODS.
Essential Precaution	**Does this mean that I have to know how the equipment will cope with the conditions created by a fault before it happens?** It means rather more than that. The Regulation requires that you know BEFORE IT IS ENERGISED how the equipment will behave. It must have the strength and capability to cope.
Strength and Capability	**How can I make an assessment of its strength and capability?** Withstand properties can be ascertained using information available in electrical specifications and tests carried out by manufacturers and accredited testing organisations based on national and international standards.
Rating	**Is the manufacturer's RATING the same as STRENGTH and CAPABILITY?** Not necessarily. Ratings are assigned by manufacturers following standardised tests. Equipment should always be used within the manufacturer's rating.
Electrical stress	**What constitutes electrically induced stress?** Electrically induced stress is the blanket term for the thermal, electro-magnetic, electro-chemical or other effects of electric currents which might be expected to flow when the equipment is part of a system. These currents include load currents, transient overloads, fault currents, pulses of current and, for alternating current circuits, currents at various power factors and frequencies. Insulation must be effective to enable the equipment to withstand the applied voltage and any transient over-voltage.
Other forms of stress	The other forms of stress which electrical equipment may be at risk from are the subject of the next section of this unit.

3.2.4. Regulation 6: Adverse or hazardous environments

Electrical equipment which may reasonably foreseeably be exposed to:

a) *mechanical damage;*

b) *the effects of the weather, natural hazards, temperature or pressure;*

c) *the effects of wet, dirty, dusty or corrosive conditions; or*

d) *any flammable or explosive substance, including dust, vapours or gases,*

shall be of such construction or as necessary protected as to prevent, so far as is reasonably practicable, danger arising from such exposure.

The Regulation simply states that equipment must be protected from any conditions which would give rise to danger so long as these conditions are reasonably foreseeable.

Suitable protection must be provided against hazardous environments. These can vary considerably with place and time, and the protection necessary will depend upon the nature of the hazard, and the degree of danger which may result.

The conditions which might give rise to danger do not have to be present before precautions are required. The precautions have to be taken if it is reasonably forseeable that the conditions might occur.

Some typical examples of the hazards to which electrical equipment may be exposed, follow.

3.2.4.1. Hazards

HAZARD	EXAMPLES
Mechanical damage	Impact, stress, strain, abrasion, wear, vibration, pneumatic and hydraulic pressure.
Weather	Long term - temperature cycling; corrosion, dust accumulation. Short term - rain, snow, ice, wind.
Natural hazards	Any hazard which is not the result of human activity, e.g. solar radiation (which can cause insulation to deteriorate), animals (gnawing by rats and mice), lightning, etc.
Temperature, pressure	The temperature of equipment may be raised by heat generated within the equipment or from a source external to it, or by the build up of detritus.
Liquids and vapours	Water (liquid), immersion, splashing, spraying, condensation. Water (vapour), solvents (solvent vapour), detergents. Conducting and non-conducting liquids may present different aspects of electrical danger.
Dirty conditions	These will include all contamination from liquids or solids (electrically conducting and non-conducting dusts may present different aspects of electrical danger).
Corrosive conditions	Those resulting from the chemical or electro-chemical action of substances singly or in combination or in the presence of water.
Flammable substances	Flammable dusts, flammable vapours
Explosive substances	Any mixture of solids, liquids, vapours or gases which are capable of exploding, e.g. petrol vapour and air; and also substances intended to explode, e.g. gunpowder.

The limitations of space and your time makes it impossible to give examples of the protection which would be suitable for the full range of electrical equipment in all the environments which are likely to be encountered. But we can illustrate just some of the protective measures which may be adopted against some of the hazards by taking one item of electrical equipment as an example.

3.2.4.2. Protecting an electric motor against damage.

HAZARD	MEANS OF PROTECTION
Mechanical damage	Protective enclosure, designed to withstand the form of mechanical damage the motor may be exposed to.
Weather	If the motor is used indoors the building should provide adequate weather protection. If used outdoors it should be enclosed in a suitably weather-proofed enclosure.
Natural hazards	The nature of the protection required will depend upon the hazard. However, measures taken to protect against non-natural hazards may be equally effective against these, e.g. a container capable of resisting mechanical damage may require little or no modification to provide protection against attack by rats and mice.
Extreme conditions of temperature and pressure	1. Appropriate means of dissipating excess heat should be incorporated in the design of the motor. 2. A suitably designed container could provide protection against extremes of temperature, pressure and humidity. 3. Accumulations of dust which would cause overheating should be removed.
Dirty conditions	1. The motor, or its enclosure, should be designed and constructed to resist the entry of dirt and dust where this can lead to electrical and/or mechanical failure. 2. Equipment which is not protected in this way should be inspected and cleaned at regular intervals as part of the maintenance programme.
Corrosive environment creating the risk of: i) accelerated corrosion of metal components ii) damage to insulation and other materials/equipment from solvents or chemical agents	1. The motor should be enclosed in a corrosion resistant housing 2. It should not be ventilated to the corrosive atmosphere, a requirement which will make the problem of dissipating any heat, generated internally, more difficult 3. The container enclosing the motor may need to be kept purged or pressurised with clean air.
Liquids and vapours	If the motor is to be used in wet or damp conditions it should be suitably housed in a water proof casing. Remember it is the second digit of an Index of Protection (IP) number, ranging in value from 0 to 8 which indicates the degree of protection. Protection against vapour can be achieved either by making the container air-tight or by purging it or positively pressurising it with air or an appropriate gas to prevent the entry of any gas or vapour from outside the container.

106

Combustible dusts

i) A layer of such dust is a fire
    hazard if it is close to a source
    of heat

ii) A cloud of combustible dust
    gives rise to the risk of an explosion.
    Protection against explosion
    is looked at in the next section

1. The dust should not be able to get into the motor
   enclosure or failing that, into the motor itself.
   IP numbers indicate the protection an enclosure
   offers against the entry of dusts and liquids.

2. No dust should be allowed to accumulate to
   where it may be ignited by a spark from the motor.

3. Any surface on which the dust settles must be at a
   temperature lower than that at which the dust
   would char and smoke.

Potentially explosive atmospheres

1. The motor should be so constructed that it is not
   liable to ignite the atmosphere.

2. The selection and installation of equipment for use
   in potentially explosive atmospheres should be
   guided by the recommendations contained in the
   HSE guidance and British standards on the subject.

3. The choice should be made from equipment which
   has been certified as being in conformity with the
   appropriate standard.

4. Uncertified electrical equipment should NOT be
   used unless it will provide at least an equivalent level
   of safety to that provided by appropriately certified
   equipment.

5. It may be possible to house the motor outside the
   area affected by the explosive atmosphere. The
   apparatus powered by the motor would then be
   separated from it by a seal which would prevent
   the electrical equipment coming into contact with
   the explosive atmosphere.

NOTE: **The maintenance and repair of explosion
       protected equipment is a specialised field of work
       and should be undertaken only by those who have
       the necessary training and experience.**

To complete Unit 2 we would now like you to attempt the self-assessment questions which
follow.

3.2.5. Self Assessment Question Test

1. SAQ - Strength and Capability of Electrical Equipment

Tick the option which completes the following statement correctly.

The phrase 'strength and capability of electrical equipment' refers to the ability of the equipment to withstand.

a) only electrically related stress.

b) both electrically related stress and mechanical damage.

c) both electrically related stress and the physical stress of a hostile environment.

d) all the stress or damage, from whatever source, that it might be subjected to in the course of its working life.

2. SAQ - Strength and Capability Rating

Indicate which of the following statements are true or false by ringing the appropriate letter.

a) The strength and capability of electrical equipment is the same as its rating.   T/F

b) The rating of equipment is usually assigned by the manufacturer.   T/F

c) The suitability of individual items of equipment chosen to meet the requirements of the Regulations is best judged using the manufacturers' ratings.   T/F

d) An assessment of the withstand properties of electrical equipment should be based on the results of accredited tests.   T/F

3. SAQ - Fault conditions

What two factors should be considered when evaluating the safety of a particular item of electrical equipment under prospective fault conditions?

Use the space below for your answer.

1. _____

2. _____

4. SAQ - Environmental Effects

The conditions at which Regulation 6 is directed are those occurring naturally as well as man-made. List four examples in the space below.

1. _____

2. _____

3. _____

4. _____

5. SAQ - Hazards

Complete the following statements.

    a)   An electric motor used in a corrosive atmosphere can be protected by being

    _____

    _____

    _____

    b)   Equipment which is to be used in an atmosphere containing solvent vapour which will attack electrical insulation should be protected by being

    _____

    _____

    _____

    c)   The maximum temperature of any surface where combustible dust may be deposited should be

    _____

    _____

    _____

    d)   Uncertified equipment should not be used unless

    _____

    _____

    _____

Turn over the page when you are satisfied with your answers.

1. Response - SAQ - Strength and Capability of Electrical Equipment

Tick the option which completes the following statement correctly.

The phrase 'strength and capability of electrical equipment' refers to the ability of the equipment to withstand.

a) only electrically related stress. ✔

b) both electrically related stress and mechanical damage.

c) both electrically related stress and the physical stress of a hostile environment.

d) all the stress or damage, from whatever source, that it might be subjected to in the course of its working life.

The correct option is (a). The complete statement should read as follows:

The phrase 'strength and capability of electrical equipment' refers to the ability of the equipment to withstand only electrically related stress.

2. Response - SAQ - Strength and Capability Rating

a) The strength and capability of electrical equipment is the same as its rating. T/**F**

This statement is false. The strength and capability of electrical equipment is not necessarily the same as its rating.

b) The rating of equipment is usually assigned by the manufacturer. **T**/F

This statement is true. The rating is usually assigned by the manufacturer following a number of tests.

c) The suitability of individual items of equipment chosen to meet the requirements of the Regulations is best judged using the manufacturers' ratings. **T**/F

This statement is true. A knowledge of the ratings will help the user to identify the withstand properties of the equipment so that any selected will comply with Regulation 5.

d) An assessment of the withstand properties of electrical equipment should be based on the results of accredited tests. **T**/F

This statement is true. The test are usually based on the requirements of national or international standards.

3. Response - SAQ - Fault conditions

What two factors should be considered when evaluating the safety of a particular item of electrical equipment under prospective fault conditions?

The two factors are:

1. the fault level;

2. the characteristics of the devices protecting the equipment against excess current.

4. Response - SAQ - Environmental Effects

The conditions at which Regulation 6 is directed are those occurring naturally as well as man-made. Your list should include any four of the following:

1. mechanical damage;

2. effects of the weather;

3. natural hazards (animals, solar radiation etc.);

4. temperature and pressure;

5. liquids and vapours;

6. dirt;

7. corrosive conditions;

8. flammable substances;

9. explosive substances.

5. Response - SAQ - Hazards

Your answers should agree with the following statements:

a) An electric motor used in a corrosive atmosphere can be protected by being **totally enclosed in a casing not ventilated to the corrosive atmosphere and made of some appropriately resistant material.**

b) Equipment which is to be used in an atmosphere containing solvent vapour which will attack electrical insulation should be protected by being **enclosed in a cubicle which is either purged or pressurised with fresh air (inert gases in special cases).**

c) The maximum temperature of any surface where combustible dust may be deposited should be **below that at which charring or smoking takes place.**

d) Uncertified equipment should not be used unless **it will provide at least an equivalent level of safety to that provided by appropriately certified equipment.**

3.2.6. Summary Of Key Points

- It must be known, BEFORE it is energised, that equipment can cope with any electrical stress it is likely to encounter in a system.

- Regulation 5 applies to all electrical equipment including that provided for protective purposes.

- The manufacturer's rating of a piece of equipment is not necessarily the same as its strength and capability.

- Protection need only be provided against reasonably foreseeable conditions.

- IP number indicates the protection an enclosure offers against the entry of dusts and liquids.

- Dust should be removed from electrical equipment to:
  (i) allow heat generated in the equipment to dissipate;
  (ii) prevent combustible dust being ignited by heat generated.

- Electrical equipment, to be used in potentially explosive atmospheres, should be chosen only from that certified as being in conformity with an appropriate standard.

- Uncertified equipment should provide at least the same level of protection.

UNIT 3

3.3.1. Aim

The aim of this unit is to familiarise you with the content of Regulations 7 and 10 and the implications of the requirements set out in these Regulations.

Objectives

When you have worked through this unit you will be able to:

- explain how the danger that Regulation 7 is aimed to prevent arises;
- list the factors which should be taken into account when considering the insulation and spacing of conductors to prevent danger;
- state the two factors which dictate the quality and effectiveness required of electrical insulation;
- list the precautions which may be taken when work is necessary in the vicinity of live and uninsulated conductors;
- list the range of connections to which Regulation 10 applies;
- state what is required of the joints and connections in a system to meet the requirements of Regulation 10;
- explain what the Regulation requires of plug and socket connections.

3.3.2. Overview

Regulation 7 is concerned with the precautions required to ensure that conductors remain safe when they are energised. A consideration of the implications of this Regulation forms the first part of the unit. The second part focuses on the requirements of Regulation 10. In it, the requirements made of the mechanical and electrical properties of joints and connections in systems are reviewed.

3.3.3. Regulation 7: Insulation, Protection and Placing of Conductors

> *All conductors in a system which may give rise to danger shall either:*
>
> *a)* *be suitably covered with insulating material and as necessary protected so as to prevent, so far as is reasonably practicable, danger; or*
>
> *b)* *have such precautions taken in respect of them (including, where appropriate, their being suitably placed) as will prevent, so far as is reasonably practicable, danger.*

The purpose of Regulation 7 is to ensure that no danger will arise from any conductors in a system.

3.3.3.1. Insulation

Insulation is the most common means of preventing contact with a current carrying conductor. It provides effective protection against the risk of injury.

What are the dangers which insulation eliminates?

The dangers fall into two categories:

  i)   electrocution as a consequence of making simultaneous contact between two conductors at different potentials;

  ii)   burns, fire and explosion, as a result of the sparking and arcing, which may occur when two conductors at different potentials are allowed to make contact. Energy from quite low voltage levels can ignite a flammable atmosphere.

What dictates the standard of insulation required?

The quality and effectiveness of insulation should be:

  i)   capable of providing effective protection over the range of voltages the equipment is designed to operate at;

  ii)   able to remain effective under the conditions of use.

What must insulation be protected against?

We have already seen in the previous unit the sorts of environment that may damage insulation with potentially dangerous results. The sources of damage are:

  i)   impact, abrasion, etc.

  ii)   wet and damp conditions;

  iii) temperature changes;

  iv)   chemical/solvent attack;

  v)   solar radiation.

3.3.3.2. How can protection be effected?

1. Before a decision can be made about the protection the uninsulated conductors may require, the following questions must be answered.

a) How is the equipment to be used and what are the consequences of that use?

b) What activities will be taking place in the immediate vicinity?

c) What are the hazards in the area where the conductors will be used other than those identified in 'a' and 'b'?

A decision can be made on the basis of this analysis, on the measures necessary to prevent danger.

These measures may include:

i) placing the insulated conductor out of the way of any risk of physical or chemical damage;

ii) placing the insulated conductor inside a protective enclosure, e.g. ducting, etc;

iii) providing the insulated conductor with an armoured sheath.

3.3.3.3. Uninsulated conductors - alternative precautions

Regulation 7 allows precautions, other than insulation, to be taken where it is necessary to use bare conductors in a system e.g. electric power lines, down-shop conductors for overhead travelling cranes in factories, etc., railway electrification and certain large electrolytic and electrothermal plants.

Regulation 14 addresses the situation where, either permanently or temporarily, danger from conductors is not prevented by the precautions specified in Regulation 7(a).

Uninsulated conductors are a source of danger and so measures must be taken to prevent injury. The measures fall into two categories:

a) Those which are intended to keep people away from the conductors. Examples of these are:

    i) secured enclosures;

    ii) barriers;

    iii) placing the conductors in an area where no one will come into contact with them during foreseeable work activity;

    iv) posting warning notices;

    v) providing appropriate training for anyone whose work is likely to take them into the vicinity of the conductors.

b) Those which are intended to prevent injury if work must take place close to the exposed conductors. For work to be done on or close to those conductors live, the conditions set out in Regulation 14 must be satisfied. Injuries may be suffered either as a result of making direct contact with the conductors or inadvertently shorting them.

Examples of the precautions which might be taken are listed below.

    i) Segregating the conductors and restricting entry to the area only to those people who have the necessary expertise and training to avoid injury.

    ii) Posting warning notices around the area.

    iii) Placing conductors, which are at different potentials, in such a way that they cannot be inadvertently connected or touched simultaneously.

    iv) Reducing conducting material in the area to a minimum.

    v) Using protective equipment, e.g. clothing, insulating mats, etc.

    vi) Providing earth-free working areas.

    vii) Using power supplies which are not earth-referenced, (i.e. isolated from earth).

3.3.4. Regulation 10: Connections

Where necessary to prevent danger, every joint and connection in a system shall be mechanically and electrically suitable for use.

The Regulation applies to all connections whether permanent or temporary. The defence out lined in Regulation 29 is available in any proceedings for an offence under this Regulation.

3.3.4.1. What is meant by being 'mechanically and electrically suitable for use'?

To fulfil this requirement:

i)   insulation and conductance should be suitable to meet all the likely demands of use, including fault conditions;

ii) the protection and mechanical strength of any connection should be capable of maintaining the integrity of the insulation and conductance of the connection under all the conditions likely to be met in (i).

NOTE: Protective conductors may require particular attention because of the environment in which they might be placed. Connections in protective conductors should be made at least as carefully as those in circuit conductors. Wet or damp conditions encourage corrosion and in this instance steps should be taken to prevent it. Certain combinations of metals corrode very quickly in damp conditions because of damaging electrolytic action. Care should be taken when selecting equipment to make sure that these combinations are not used. If this cannot be avoided, the equipment should not be placed in an environment where an electrolytic reaction can take place.

3.3.4.2. Plugs and Sockets

In order to meet the requirements of Regulation 10 any plug or socket used in a system should have at least one or other of the following features, as the need demands.

i)   They should not expose anyone to the risk of inadvertently touching a live conductor at a dangerous voltage. The choice of appropriate equipment should usually be sufficient to prevent this, but some training may also be required.

ii) If a protective conductor (earth wire) is to be included in a plug/socket combination, safety can only be assured if it is designed so that the earth contact breaks last and is made first. In this way, the protective conductor is always functional while current flows.

iii) When a connection is not rated to be made or broken when the maximum load current is flowing, it should be constructed in such a way that contact is only made or broken under no-load conditions.

NOTE: (i) and (ii) are met by a plug and socket made to BS 1363A or BS 4343. The joints and connections in cables used with portable equipment are likely to be exposed to more damaging environments and conditions of use, than fixed equipment. Generally any equipment or cables which are handled are prone to mechanical damage and so they require special attention to ensure safety. They should be constructed in accordance with the appropriate standards. Where the metal casing of such equipment is earthed, this precaution should be effected automatically when the equipment is connected to a power supply. Now attempt the self-assessment questions which follow.

3.3.5. Self Assessment Question Test

1. SAQ - Danger

Regulation 7 is intended to prevent such danger as fire, explosion, electrocution and the injuries which may result. What is the root cause of these dangers in an electrical system? Use the space below for your answer.

_____

_____

_____

_____

_____

2. SAQ - Insulation and separation

Which of the following factors should be taken into account so that the separation and insulation of conductors meets the requirements of Regulation 7?

Tick your choice.

a) The minimum functional requirement for both insulation and separation.

b) The nature of the work associated with the equipment.

c) The range of environments which might be experienced.

d) The nature and degree of any danger which may arise.

e) The designed function of the equipment.

3. SAQ - Conductor insulation

What two general factors dictate the quality and effectiveness required of an insulator?

Tick the answer which you think is correct.

a) The conditions of use and the applied voltage.

b) The applied voltage and the quality of the maintenance programme.

c) The quality of the maintenance programme and whether the current in the conductor is alternating or direct.

d) The conditions of use and whether the current in the conductor is alternating or direct.

4. SAQ - Measures other than insulation, to prevent danger arising from uninsulated conductors.

If conductors are not insulated they are a source of danger. The precautions that can be taken to prevent injury fall into two categories:

    i)   those which keep people away from the danger;

    ii)   those which prevent injury if the danger area has to be entered.

List the precautions which might be taken in the appropriate space below.

    i)   Precautions required to keep people away from uninsulated conductors.

_____

_____

    ii)   Precautions required to prevent injury when working in the vicinity of uninsulated conductors.

_____

_____

_____

5. SAQ - Connections

    a)   Answer the following questions by ringing the appropriate letters.

        i)   Does Regulation 10 apply to both permanent and temporary connections?   Y/N

        ii)   Does it apply to all connections and joints in both circuit and protective conductors?   Y/N

    b)   What electrical requirements does Regulation 10 make of a connection? Write your answer in the space below.

_____

_____

_____

    c)   What mechanical requirements does Regulation 10 make of a connection? Write your answer in the space below.

_____

_____

_____

    d)   The joints and connections used in protective conductors may require special precautions to be taken. What are these precautions? Write your answer in the space below.

_____

_____

_____

You will find the answers to these questions on the next page.

1. Response - SAQ - Danger

> Regulation 7 is intended to prevent such danger as fire, explosion, electrocution and the injuries which may result. What is the root cause of these dangers in an electrical system?

The root cause of the danger is the difference in potential which may exist betwen circuit conductors and between circuit conductors and the other conductors in a system.

2. Response - SAQ - Insulation and separation

> Which of the following factors should be taken into account so that the separation and insulation of conductors meets the requirements of Regulation 7?

Your list should look like this:

a)   The minimum functional requirement for both insulation and separation. ☐

b)   The nature of the work associated with the equipment. ✔

c)   The range of environments which might be experienced. ✔

d)   The nature and degree of any danger which may arise. ✔

e)   The designed function of the equipment. ✔

The only one which remains unticked is the minimum functional requirement for both insulation and separation. The minimum functional requirement may not meet the requirement of Regulation 7 which is to prevent danger.

3. Response - SAQ - Conductor insulation

> What two general factors dictate the quality and effectiveness required of an insulator?

The correct answer is (a). The two general factors which dictate the quality and effectiveness required of an insulator are the conditions of use and the applied voltage.

Insulation is the primary and necessary safeguard to prevent electric shock. In addition it prevents the fires and explosions which can result from sparking or arcing in the presence of flammable or explosive materials. The protection is afforded only so long as the insulation remains intact.

The condition of use, the environment the conductor is placed in and the likelihood of physical damage have a direct influence on the quality and effectiveness required of the insulation.

The applied voltage is also directly relevant. The greater the voltage the thicker the insulating layer must be to prevent arcing.

4. Response - SAQ -   Measures other than insulation, to prevent danger arising from uninsulated conductors.

If conductors are not insulated they are a source of danger.

The precautions that can be taken to prevent injury, fall into two categories:

    i)   those which keep people away from the danger;

    ii)   those which prevent injury if the danger area has to be entered.

List the precautions which might be taken in the appropriate space below.

Precautions required to keep people away from uninsulated conductors.

- Place the conductors where contact cannot be made if agreed working practices are followed.

- Erect barriers.

- Place warning notices.

- Locate the conductors within a secure enclosure.

Precautions required to prevent injury when working in the vicinity of uninsulated conductors.

- Place warning notices.

- Limit entry to the area to only those people with the appropriate training and expertise.

- Ensure adequate supervision.

- Provide protective equipment, clothing, insulated mats, etc.

- Establish an earth-free environment within the working area.

- Use electrical supplies which are isolated from earth.

- Install protective devices to ensure the electrical supply remains isolated from earth.

- Locate conductors which are at different potentials in such a way that they cannot be inadvertently connected.

- Exclude all unnecessary conducting material from the area.

5. Response - SAQ - Connections

    a)   Answer the following questions by ringing the appropriate letters.

        i)   Does Regulation 10 apply to both permanent and temporary connections?

        ii)   Does it apply to all connections and joints in both circuit and protective conductors.

    b)   What electrical requirements does Regulation 10 make of a connection?

Regulation 10 requires that the insulation and conductance of connections should be suitable, taking into account all the conditions of use including likely fault conditions.

c) What mechanical requirements does Regulation 10 make of a connection?

The mechanical protection and strength of a connection must be such that the integrity of its insulation and conductance is ensured under all conditions of use including likely fault conditions.

d) The joints and connections used in protective conductors may require special precautions to be taken. What are these precautions?

The connections may require special treatment to protect them from corrosion. A corroded connection may represent a significant electrical resistance in the protective conductor which may have very serious consequences in the event of a fault occurring. As an additional precaution, care should be taken to avoid using combinations of different metals, which might result in corrosion-accelerating electrolytic action.

3.3.6. Summary of Key points

- Insulation is the most commonly used method of preventing:

    i) contact with a current carrying conductor;

    ii) inadvertent contact between conductors at different potentials.

- The primary purpose of any protection provided for an insulated conductor is to prevent damage to the insulation.

- The suitable placing of uninsulated conductors may be sufficient to ensure safety.

- Where placing alone does not guarantee safety, any other precaution which is considered to be necessary must be rigorously applied.

- The insulation and conductance of a connection should be suitable for all conditions of use including fault conditions.

- The protection and strength of a connection should be sufficient to maintain the integrity of its insulation and conductance under all conditions of use.

- Care should be taken to prevent the corrosion of connections in protective conductors.

- Plugs and sockets should be so constructed that they do not present a danger, under any foreseeable conditions, when used for the purpose for which they were intended.

- The joints and connections in any equipment which is handled, require special attention because they are more prone to mechanical damage.

UNIT 4

3.4.1. Aim:

The aim of this unit is to familiarise you with the contents of Regulations 8 and 9, and the implications of their requirements.

Objectives

When you have worked through this unit you will be able to:

- explain what is considered to be a conductor for the purposes of the Regulations;

- list the dangers which may arise if precautions are not taken to make a charged non-circuit conductor safe;

- describe the three general methods of eliminating the danger associated with a charged conductor, together with the associated techniques;

- explain the circumstances which would permit the placing of an electrical device in a referenced conductor;

- explain the danger which arises if the integrity of a combined neutral and earth conductor is not maintained;

- explain the placing of fuses and switches in the conductors of a system having a separate neutral and protective conductor.

3.4.2. Overview

This unit is concerned with the interpretation of Regulations 8 and 9.

There is a close link between the two. The purpose of Regulation 8 is to ensure that danger shall not arise in the event of a non-circuit conductor becoming charged. Chief amongst the precautions discussed in our review of Regulation 8, which forms the first part of the unit, is earthing. This safety measure, which has almost universal application, forms the link between the two Regulations, because in Part 2 we look at the implications of the requirements set out in Regulation 9. The purpose of this Regulation is to safeguard the integrity of referenced conductors, the vast majority of which are referenced to earth.

In Part 1, the three general methods of preventing danger arising from the charging of non-circuit conductors are set out, together with their supporting techniques which you have already met in Module 2.

In Part 2 we expand upon the precautions to be taken to maintain the integrity of neutral or neutral/earth conductors.

We have departed from the usual custom of having a single self-assessment question test at the end of the unit. There are two tests in this unit, one at the end of Part 1, and the other at the end of Part 2.

The unit closes with a summary of the key points.

3.4.3. Regulation 8: Earthing or other suitable precautions

Precautions shall be taken, either by earthing or other suitable means, to prevent danger arising when any conductor (other than a circuit conductor) which may reasonably foreseeably become charged as a result of either the use of a system, or a fault in a system, becomes so charged; and, for the purposes of ensuring compliance with this Regulation, a conductor shall be regarded as earthed when it is connected to the general mass of earth by conductors of sufficient strength and current-carrying capability to discharge electrical energy to earth.

The purpose of Regulation 8 is to prevent danger arising when any conductor, other than a circuit conductor, becomes charged. The defence outlined in Regulation 29 is available in any proceedings for an offence under this Regulation.

3.4.3.1. What is a conductor for the purpose of Regulation 8?

We have already seen that any material which is capable of conducting electricity is a conductor for the purpose of the Regulations. The conductors which are the subject of Regulation 8 may include:

a)   the conductive parts of equipment, which although not normally live, may become live as the result of a fault;

b)   conductors which, although not part of a system and not normally live, may become so as a result of:

      i)   a fault;

      ii)   being close enough to the system to be energised by electrostatic or electromagnetic effects. (If these induced currents and voltages are large enough to give rise to danger, appropriate precautions would have to be taken).

So Regulation 8 may be far reaching in its application.

3.4.3.2. The dangers which may arise if precautions are not taken.

The danger referred to in the Regulation is the risk of injury from electricity. As we have already seen, these injuries fall into two categories:

    i)   those inflicted directly by electricity;

    ii)   those which result from an event triggered by electricity, such as fire and explosion.

3.4.3.3. The general methods employed to comply with Regulation 8

Electric shock and burn can result from contact with a conductor at a dangerous potential while being in simultaneous contact with earth or a conductor at earth potential. Sparking and arcing can occur when two conductors at different potentials are brought into contact.

As we have already seen there are three general methods employed to eliminate these dangers. These are:

    i)   ensure that the conductors covered by Regulation 8 do not become charged; or

    ii)   ensure that if they do become charged, the values and duration of any transient current or voltage, do not give rise to danger; or

    iii)   ensure that the environment is such that if the conductors become charged, no danger arises.

3.4.4. The techniques employed

Each of the general methods makes use of one or more techniques to achieve their aims. Reference was made to them in Module 2, but to refresh your memory we will outline them again in association with the particular general method they support.

3.4.4.1. Ensure that the conductors covered by Regulation 8 do not become charged

Double insulation: Two discrete layers of insulation are used instead of one. Each layer alone, is capable of ensuring that the conductor it protects cannot give rise to danger, under normal conditions of use, including fault conditions.

Double insulation removes the need for an earth conductor, and has been found to be particularly suitable for portable equipment. However, danger is eliminated only so long as the insulation remains intact. For this reason, the maintenance of such equipment is of great importance.

3.4.4.2. Ensure that the values and duration of any transient current or voltage, do not give rise to danger.

a) Earthing: The public supply in the UK is referenced to earth by a deliberate earth connection at the distribution sub-station or power transformer. This makes it possible to:

i)   detect earth faults on electrical equipment;

ii)   disconnect faulty equipment automatically.

Automatic disconnection: Automatic disconnection is made possible by protective devices such as circuit breakers or fuses. The fault current must be large enough to operate the protective device quickly so that the power supply is interrupted before damage and injury can result. In most cases the devices are selected to provide the additional protective function of interrupting excess of current, as required by Regulation 11.

Magnitude of the fault current: The magnitude of the fault current is determined largely by the impedance of the earth fault loop, which is made up of four components.

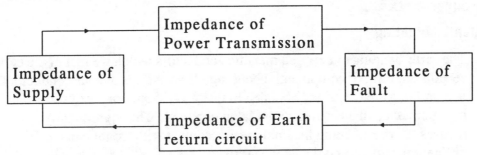

The IEE Wiring Regulations lists acceptable parameters for earth fault loop impedances and the interruption times of protective devices.

Earth Conductors: If the earth conductor fails either because it becomes open circuit or because a large impedance is introduced into it, protection is removed. **Consequently, the integrity of the earth conductor is of the greatest importance.**

b) Connection to a common voltage reference point

In the last section we saw the benefits to be gained if the power supply is referenced to earth. However, reference points other than earth may be chosen to suit particular circumstances. This ocurs only in a few very specialised circumstances.

c) Use of safe voltages

It is internationally recognised that a system operating on 50 volts a.c. or 120 volts d.c. is safe in most circumstances. It is particularly suitable for use with portable equipment and where the risk of physical damage to equipment is high. Such a supply is recognised internationally as safe, in normal dry conditions but in highly conducting areas, e.g. where there is water or a significant amount of exposed metal, it can still represent a hazard. Consequently, it is recommended that the precautions taken with standard power supplies should also be taken in this case, e.g. earthing and bonding, or the use of separated or isolated systems (see (c) below).

d) Current limitation

When a person receives an electric shock their survival depends on the speed with which the protective devices interrupt the supply. The time which can elapse before a current proves fatal depends upon a variety of factors, including the health of the victim, but chief amongst them is the size of the current.

A current of 1 milliamp will give a sensation of shock to most people. A current of 100 milliamps would quickly prove fatal in most cases.

If the maximum current which could flow through the victim is limited to 1 milli amp or at the most 5 milliamps the need for earthing could be removed, because currents of this size are not generally life threatening. However, they might still give rise to injuries, for example, from a fall caused by the shock sensation. Remember that this type of consequential injury is not covered by these Regulations.

The current can be limited to an acceptable level by placing a suitably high resistance in the phase conductor.

3.4.4.3. Ensure that the environment is such that, if the conductors become charged, no danger arises.

a) Equipotential bonding

The earth-bonding of exposed metallic conductors which we met in the earthing section is a form of equipotential bonding. If all the extraneous conductors in a building are electrically bonded in this way, should one be raised to a high potential, all are raised to the same potential. This significantly reduces the risk of being in simultaneous contact with conductors at different potentials and the attendant risks.

b) Earth-free non-conducting environment

The elimination of any conductor at earth potential from an area simultaneously removes the path to earth for any fault current and any dangerous potentials to earth. In such an earth-free environment there is no risk of electric shock, burn, fire or explosion. Constructing such an area can be costly and so they are reserved for specialised applications such as the testing of particular types of electrical equipment. The greatest practical disadvantage is the difficulty of monitoring the integrity of the earth-free area against the fortuitous introduction of earth potentials.

c) Separated or isolated systems

If a supply is not referenced to earth or any other part of its immediate environment, in theory, no potential should exist between the conductors energised by it and earth. Consequently no current will flow to earth and the risk of shock, etc. is removed. In practice it is very difficult to guarantee this electrical isolation and so it cannot be safely assumed that any system supplied from such a source will continue to be at zero potential relative to earth.

Additional precautions will usually be necessary, such as the use of an earth-free non-conducting environment or earth fault detection.

Regular inspection to ensure that isolation is being maintained will also be necessary.

That completes the first part of Unit 4. The self-assessment test follows.

3.4.5. Self-Assessment Question Test

1. SAQ - Conductors covered by Regulation 8

Which of the following conductors are subject to the requirements of Regulation 8?

Place a tick beside your choice.

- a) The earth conductor in a domestic system.
- b) The metal case of an electric drill which is provided with an earth lead.
- c) The metal case of a double-insulated electric drill which is not provided with an earth lead.
- d) The neutral conductor in a factory's power system.

2. SAQ - The dangers arising from failure to take precautions against the charging of non-circuit conductors

If precautions are not taken and a conductor becomes energised, but only at a voltage where there is no danger of shock, what risks may still remain? Write your answer in the space below.

_____

_____

_____

_____

3. SAQ - Eliminating danger

Link the techniques listed below with the appropriate general method of ensuring safety when a conductor becomes energised. Show the link by writing the techniques number in the appropriate box.

1. Double insulation
2. Earthing
3. Equipotential bonding
4. Use of safe voltages
5. Earth-free non-conducting environments

Ensuring that such conductors do not become charged.	
Ensuring that if such conductors do become charged, the values of voltage and current and their duration are such that danger will not arise.	
Ensuring that if such conductors do become charged, the environment is such that danger will not arise.	

1. Response - SAQ Conductors covered by Regulation 8

Which of the following conductors are subject to the requirements of Regulation 8?

Your list should look like this.

a)   The earth conductor in a domestic system.   ✓

b)   The metal case of an electric drill which is provided
with an earth lead.   ✓

c)   The metal case of a double-insulated electric drill
which is not provided with an earth lead.   ☐

d)   The neutral conductor in a factory's power system.   ✓

The only option which remains unticked is (c). So long as care is taken with the design, construction and maintenance of doubly insulated equipment, there should be no risk of a non-circuit conductor becoming charged.

This has the effect of excluding the metal case from the scope of the Regulation.

2. Response - SAQ The dangers arising from failure to take precautions against the charging of non-circuit conductors.

If precautions are not taken and a conductor becomes energised, but only at a voltage where there is no danger of shock, what risks may still remain?

Even if the voltage is at a level where there is no risk of shock, sparking and arcing can still occur. If flammable material is close enough to the discharge to be ignited there is the risk of fire or explosion.

3. Response - SAQ Eliminating danger

Link the techniques listed below with the appropriate general method of ensuring safety when a conductor becomes energised.

1. Double insulation.

2. Earthing.

3. Equipotential bonding.

4. Use of safe voltages.

5. Earth-free non-conducting environments.

Your grid should look like this.

Ensuring that such conductors do not become charged.	1
Ensuring that if such conductors do become charged the values of voltage and current and their duration are such that danger will not arise.	2. 4.
Ensuring that if such conductors do become charged the environment is such that danger will not arise.	3. 5.

3.4.6. Regulation 9 Integrity of referenced conductors

If a circuit conductor is connected to earth or to any other reference point, nothing which might reasonably be expected to give rise to danger by breaking the electrical continuity or introducing high impedance shall be placed in that conductor unless suitable precautions are taken to prevent that danger.

The purpose of Regulation 9 is to remove any danger should a fault occur by ensuring that the impedance of a circuit conductor's earth connection remains low while the system is energised.

The defence outlined in Regulation 29 is available in any proceedings for an offence under this Regulation.

3.4.6.1. Common systems to which Regulation 9 is relevant

In the majority of situations, as we have already seen, the power supply is referenced to earth. The most common system is one in which the neutral conductor is connected to earth.

There are two ways of doing this:

i)   **Separate neutral and protective conductors both connected to earth.**

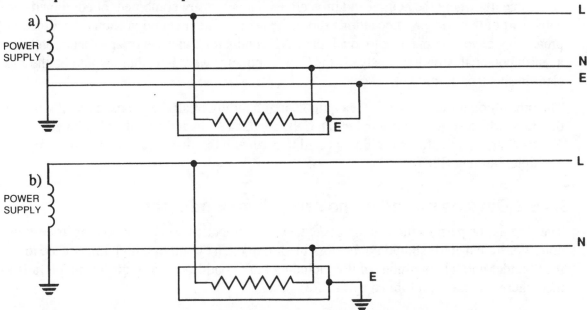

Both the systems shown have separate neutral and protective conductors. In system (a) use is made of the supplier's protective conductor. In system (b) the protective conductor is connected to a separate earth electrode. An effective earth connection is sometimes difficult to make using a separate earth electrode and additional safety back-up should be provided, such as a sensitive residual current device.

In both systems danger will arise if the neutral conductor should acquire a high impedance or become an open circuit. All the circuit conductors on the supply side of the open circuit will be at phase potential although the equipment would appear to be dead. Anyone working on the equipment in these circumstances would run the risk of electric shock or burn if they touched a circuit conductor while simultaneously in contact with earth. The risk of this may be high because the protective earth conductor would still be intact.

This danger can be prevented if the requirements of Regulation 9 are met.

ii) A combined neutral and protective conductor which is connected to earth.

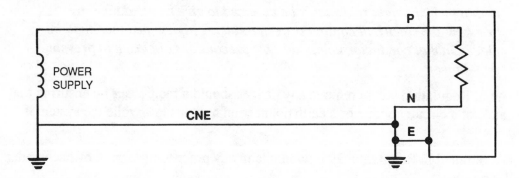

In this version of the basic system a low resistance path to earth is provided via the CNE conductor if there is a fault to the metalwork or to earth. However, if the CNE conductor were to become open circuit, conductive parts connected to it might be raised to a dangerous potential.

Consequently where the neutral and protective conductors are combined, or combined for some part of their length, precautions should be taken. The precaution should be aimed at preventing anyone being able to touch the CNE conductor and earth or any other conductor at earth potential, simultaneously. If the CNE conductor were live, there would be the risk of electric shock or burn.

The precaution usually taken is the equipotential bonding of all the exposed metal work in a building, which is then connected to the CNE conductor. In addition the Combined Neutral/Earth conductor is itself connected to earth at more than one point to give Protective Multiple Earthing (PME).

3.4.6.2. Devices placed in the protective conductor

The Regulation permits the placing of devices in a protective conductor so long as certain conditions are met. It should not be possible for an open circuit or a high impedance to result under normal conditions of use including fault conditions. Any device which fails to meet these criteria is prohibited by this Regulation.

Permitted devices would include:

i)   a proper joint;

ii)   a bolted link;

iii)   a removable link;   } Provided suitable precautions are

iv)   a manually operated knife switch.   adopted to meet the requirements already outlined.

Prohibited devices would include:

i)   fuses;

ii)   thyristors;

iii)   transistors.

3.4.6.3. Switching the neutral conductor

In general, if a neutral conductor is to be switched, the switch should interrupt both the neutral and phase conductors. It should be designed so that the neutral is not broken first and made last so that the hazards associated with an open circuit in the neutral conductor cannot arise, although the neutral may be broken and made at the same time as the phase conductor (simultaneous operation).

That completes Unit 4. Attempt the self-assessment exercise which follows.

3.4.7. Self-Assessment Question Test

1. SAQ - The placing of electrical devices in a referenced conductor.

Amend the statements listed below by deleting ONE of the words in each bracket. The amended statement must comply with Regulation 9.

a) A fuse (can/cannot) be placed in a referenced conductor because arrangements (can/cannot) be made to ensure that the device does not give rise to danger.

b) A removable link (can/cannot) be placed in a referenced conductor because arrangements (can/cannot) be made to ensure that the device does not give rise to danger.

2. SAQ - Integrity of the combined neutral and earth conductor.

If an open circuit is created in a combined neutral earth protective conductor when it is accidentally severed, what likely effect will this have on any other conductor linked to it?

Write your answer in the space below.

_____

_____

_____

_____

_____

_____

3. SAQ - General precaution to be taken with neutral conductors

Tick the option which completes the following statement correctly.

If it is necessary to switch the neutral conductor in a system which has separate neutral and protective conductors, the switch should.

a) break only the neutral conductor. ☐

b) break both the neutral and phase conductors, whilst ensuring that the neutral does not break first and make last. ☐

c) break both the neutral and phase conductors, whilst ensuring that the neutral does not break last and make first. ☐

d) break the neutral, phase and earth conductors, whilst ensuring that the earth breaks last and makes first. ☐

1. Response - SAQ   The placing of electrical devices in a referenced conductor

The correct statements should read as follows:

a)   A fuse **cannot** be placed in a referenced conductor because arrangements **cannot** be made to ensure that the device does not give rise to danger.

b)   A removable link **can** be placed in a referenced conductor because arrangements **can** be made to ensure that the device does not give rise to danger.

2. Response - SAQ   Integrity of the combined neutral and earth conductor

If an open circuit is created in a combined neutral/earth protective conductor when it is accidentally severed, what likely effect will this have on any other conductors linked to it?

An open circuit in a combined neutral/earth conductor will almost certainly mean that any devices previously earthed through the conductor will now be at a significant potential relative to earth.

This will give rise to the danger of both electric shock and electric burning.

3. Response - SAQ   General precaution to be taken with neutral conductors

Tick the option which completes the following statement correctly.

If it is necessary to switch the neutral conductor in a system which has separate neutral and protective conductors, the switch should.

a)   break only the neutral conductor. ☐

b)   break both the neutral and phase conductors, whilst ensuring that the neutral does not break first and make last. ✓

c)   break both the neutral and phase conductors, whilst ensuring that the neutral does not break last and make first. ☐

d)   break the neutral, phase and earth conductors, whilst ensuring that the earth breaks last and makes first. ☐

The correct option is (b). If it is necessary to switch the neutral conductor in a system which has separate neutral and protective conductors, the switch should break both the neutral and phase conductors, whilst ensuring that the neutral breaks last and makes first.

NOTE: The switch should not interrupt the protective conductor.

3.4.8. Summary of Key Points

- Any material which is capable of conducting electricity and which foreseeably may be energised by the use of a system or some fault in that system, must meet the requirements of Regulation 8.

- The risk of injury may be eliminated by either:

  a) ensuring such conductors do not become charged; or

  b) ensuring that if they do become charged the magnitude and duration of any voltage or current is such that there is no danger; or

  c) ensuring that if they do become charged danger does not arise because of the nature of the environment.

- The techniques used to support each of these methods of eliminating danger are:

  a) double insulation;

  b)   i) earthing;

       ii) connection to a common voltage reference point on the system;

       iii) use of safe voltages;

       iv) current limitation;

       v) separated or isolated systems;

  c)   i) earth-free, non-conducting environments;

       ii) equipotential bonding.

- The earth fault loop impedance should be low enough to allow a fault current of sufficient size to operate the protective devices.

- The protective devices used usually are selected for the dual role of clearing earth faults and limiting excess current, which is required by Regulation 11.

- A device may be placed in a referenced conductor so long as it cannot give rise to an open circuit or a high impedance under normal conditions of use, including fault conditions.

- An open circuit or a high impedance in a combined neutral and protective conductor will almost certainly result in a significant potential appearing in any non-circuit conductor linked to it.

- An open circuit or a high impedance in the neutral conductor of a system having separate neutral and protective conductors, places persons working on the system at risk from electric shock/burn.

- If a neutral conductor has to be switched, the phase conductor must be switched as well. The switch must be so designed that the neutral conductor does not break first and make last. This precaution ensures that the two hazards outlined above cannot arise.

UNIT 5

3.5.1. Aim:

The aim of this unit is to familiarise you with the contents of Regulations 11 and 12 and the interpretation which should be put on the wording of these Regulations.

Objectives

When you have worked through this unit you will be able to:

- explain how fault and overload currents may arise;
- state where protective devices should usually be placed in a circuit;
- list the criteria which should be taken into account when selecting protective equipment;
- explain what precaution should be taken should it be undesirable to interrupt the current in the circuit;
- explain the difference between cutting off the supply of electricity to equipment and isolating it;
- recognise when Regulation 12(1) would not apply to electrical equipment;
- list what is required of a suitable means of cutting off the supply;
- list what is required of a suitable means of isolation;
- explain the factors which should be taken into account when selecting isolator switches.

3.5.2. Overview

Part 1 of this unit is devoted to a consideration of Regulation 11 which requires that where excess current is a source of danger it should be controlled. The situations in which excess current can arise are briefly reviewed before we consider where, in a circuit, protective devices are usually placed. However, the greater part of this section is concerned with the criteria which should be considered when selecting protective devices. We complete our appraisal of Regulation 11 with a brief review of the precautions needed in those situations where it may be undesirable, for safety reasons, to interrupt the flow of current.

We open Part 2 by establishing the context in which the requirements of Regulation 12 are set. We define what is meant by the terms **isolation** and **switch off**, examine the implications of the exclusion clause contained in Regulation 12(3) and consider the scope of the qualifying term **where necessary to prevent danger**. The remainder of this section is devoted to the criteria which should be used to establish means of cutting off power and isolating equipment, if they are to meet the requirements of this Regulation.

3.5.3. Regulation 11: Means for protecting against excess of current

Efficient means, suitably located, shall be provided for protecting from any excess of current every part of a system as may be necessary to prevent danger.

The Regulation requires that the duty holder should take steps to prevent danger arising from an excess of current. The term **so far as is reasonably practicable** is not used and so the duty is absolute. However, in some circumstances, it may be impossible to comply totally with the Regulation because danger may exist during the brief time it takes for any protective device to operate and clear the fault. Nevertheless, the duty holder must make every effort to provide efficient and effective protection.

The defence outlined in Regulation 29 is available in any proceedings for an offence under this Regulation.

3.5.4. Causes of excess current

Excess current may result from either of the following circumstances.

i)   Short circuits between conductors caused either by faults developing within the equipment or damage being inflicted on it. The result is the same in both cases, a large current flows between the two conductors. Just how large and damaging it will be depends upon the potential difference between the two conductors and the resistance of the fault loop.

ii)   The inability of the equipment to support the load which is put on it, e.g. the mechanical overloading of an electric motor. In this example the motor slows as it fails to cope with its load, resulting in a surge of current in the motor's windings. If this were allowed to continue the windings would burn out.

3.5.5. The positioning of protective devices in circuits.

It is usual to place a protective device, usually a fuse or a circuit breaker, at the power source end of a circuit. This provides protection for the whole circuit but only against the currents in excess of the device's rated value. At each point where the rating of circuit changes (its electrical load bearing capability changes), an appropriate device should be placed to protect the lower rated section of the circuit. In this way each part of the circuit is provided with the protection it requires to safeguard against damaging currents.

A device will operate in response to an earth fault appearing on its circuit side and between it and the next lower rated circuit. Hence, Fuse A will operate if a fault appears at point A, Fuse B if a fault appears at point B, and so on.

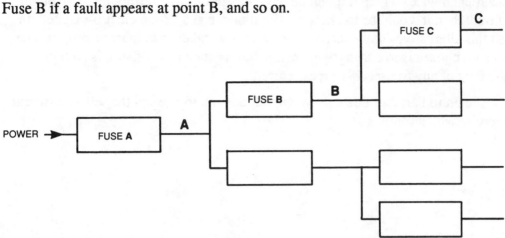

There are exceptions to this principle depending on the nature of the system, but these need not concern us here.

Discrimination

This sequence of operations, which allows fault-free circuits to continue to function while taking out only those at risk, is called **discrimination**.

3.5.6. Protecting against excess current: the selection of suitable devices

The protective device selected must be able to:

i)   operate only when potentially damaging currents flow;

ii)   respond quickly enough to prevent damage;

iii) operate without giving rise to other hazards, e.g. igniting a flammable atmosphere.

There are a number of factors to be considered if these criteria are to be applied. The most important ones are:

i)   **the nature of the circuits and equipment to be protected;**

ii)   **the size of the current which would flow in the event of a fault**; it must be large enough to operate the device while not so large that it would cause the device to operate dangerously;

iii) **the environment in which the fault current would flow and the protective device would operate;** a potentially hazardous environment would require equipment that would function without creating further danger;

iv)   **whether the system is earthed or not;** as we have already seen the efficiency of protective devices for earth faults is directly related to the nature and efficiency of the earthing system where one is used; a circuit which is protected by fuses or circuit breakers and which has an unreliable earthing system, such as an earth electrode, requires a second line of protective devices, such as sensitive residual current devices, if it is to be considered safe against faults to earth.

3.5.7. Equipment which requires alternative protection

There are electrical devices where it might be more dangerous to interrupt the flow of an excessive current than it would be to allow it to continue, e.g. a lifting electro-magnet. In cases such as this alternatives to the use of fuses, circuit breakers etc. must be sought. The most usual means chosen is to construct the equipment in such a way that it is able to withstand the flow of any foreseeable excess current.

Before you move on to Part 2 of this unit we would like you to attempt the self assessment questions exercise which follows.

3.5.8. Self-Assessment Questions Test

1. SAQ - Excess current

Indicate which of the following statements are true or false by ringing the appropriate letter.

a) Where electrical equipment is overloaded or short circuits occur there is always excess current. T/F

b) An excess current will result if two bare conductors, at different potentials, are allowed to make contact. T/F

c) An excess current may appear in the windings of an electric motor which is made to work under an excessive load. T/F

d) Where electrical equipment is overloaded, or short circuits occur, there will only be an excess of current if the conductors are not rated highly enough to withstand it. T/F

2. SAQ - Selection of excess current protection

Tick the factors which should be taken into account when selecting the means of protecting against excess current.

a) The nature of the circuits and the type of equipment to be protected. ☐

b) The short circuit energy which is available in the supply (the fault level). ☐

c) The nature of the environment. ☐

d) Whether the system is earthed or not. ☐

3. SAQ - The placing of protective devices

Tick the options which complete the following statement correctly.

Protective devices are usually placed at the point in a circuit where:

a) a fault is likely to occur; ☐

b) the rating of the circuit changes; ☐

c) it is necessary to use exposed circuit conductors; ☐

d) the circuit conductors are earthed; ☐

e) the circuit divides. ☐

1. Response - SAQ Excess current

Your list should look like this.

a) Where electrical equipment is overloaded or short circuits occur there is always excess current. (T)/F

b) An excess current will result if two bare conductors, at different potentials, are allowed to make contact. (T)/F

c) An excess current may appear in the windings of an electric motor which is made to work under an excessive load. (T)/F

d) Where electrical equipment is overloaded or short circuits occur there will only be an excess of current if the conductors are not rated highly enough to withstand it. T/(F)

The last statement (d) is false, because an excess current will always arise in these circumstances. However, if the conductors are able to withstand it, the danger is eliminated.

2. Response - SAQ Selection of excess current protection

You should have ticked the following items.

a) The nature of the circuits and the type of equipment to be protected. ✓

b) The short circuit energy available in the supply (the fault level). ✓

c) The nature of the environment. ✓

d) Whether the system is earthed or not. ✓

3. Response - SAQ The placing of protective devices

Tick the options which complete the following statement correctly.

Protective devices are usually placed at the point in a circuit where:

a) a fault is likely to occur;

b) the rating of the circuit changes; ✓

c) it is necessary to use exposed circuit conductors;

d) the circuit conductors are earthed;

e) the circuit divides. ✓

The correct options are (b) and (e). Protective devices are usually placed at the point in a circuit where the rating of the circuit changes and where the circuit divides to limit the extent of disconnections in the event of a fault.

3.5.9. Summary Of Key Points

- The duty imposed by Regulation 11 is absolute, although in some circumstances it will be technically impossible to achieve total compliance with the Regulation.

- Excess current may be caused either by a short circuit or by electrically or mechanically overloading equipment.

- It is usual to place a protective device at each point in a circuit where its rating changes, or where the circuit divides.

- Protective devices used against an excess of current, should operate only in response to an excess in the part of the circuit they are designed to protect.

- They should be capable of operating safely in response to the maximum foreseeable fault current.

- They should be capable of operating without causing danger in their designated working environment.

- The nature and efficiency of earthing systems have a direct effect on the reliability of protective devices used for protection against faults to earth.

3.5.10. Regulation 12: Means for cutting off the supply and for isolation.

1. *Subject to paragraph (3), where necessary to prevent danger, suitable means (including, where appropriate, methods of identifying circuits) shall be available for:*

   a) *cutting off the supply of electrical energy to any electrical equipment;*

   b) *the isolation of any electrical equipment.*

2. *In paragraph (1), "isolation" means the disconnection and separation of the electrical equipment from every source of electrical energy in such a way that this disconnection and separation is secure.*

3. *Paragraph (1) shall not apply to electrical equipment which is itself a source of electrical energy but, in such a case as is necessary, precautions shall be taken to prevent, so far as is reasonably practicable, danger.*

The requirement set out in Regulation 12(1) to cut off and isolate electrical equipment are not qualified by the words **so far as is reasonably practicable** and so the duty is absolute. The defence outlined in Regulation 29 is available in any proceedings for an alleged offence under this Regulation.

3.5.11. "Switching off/cutting off" and "isolation"

It is important that the difference between these two terms should be understood. When equipment is switched off it is deprived of electric power. When it is isolated, not only is it deprived of power from any source, but steps have been taken to ensure that it cannot be inadvertently re-energised.

The devices used can fulfil either the requirement of Regulation 12(1)(a) and switch off the power, or both Regulation 12(1)(a) and (b) by isolating the equipment. It is not possible to fulfil Regulation 12(1)(b) without automatically fulfilling the requirement for Regulation 12(1)(a). Safety is considerably enhanced if the risk of equipment being re-energised while work is being carried out on it, is eliminated.

3.5.12. Regulation 12(3)

In some instances, it is impossible to switch off or isolate equipment because it is the energy source or a part of it, e.g. accumulator terminals, large capacitors and the windings of generators. In cases such as these, the duty holder is required to take action to prevent danger, "so far as is reasonably practicable". Unlike Regulation 12(1), the duty outlined in Regulation 12(3) is not absolute.

Danger

Regulation 12(1) qualifies the requirement to provide suitable means of switching off and isolating equipment with the words "where necessary to prevent danger". The duty holder must anticipate any danger that might arise during both normal and abnormal conditions. Anticipation of the need to switch off power and isolate particular systems or parts of systems should be part of the emergency planning process.

3.5.13. Cutting off the supply: what requirements must be met before the means of cutting off the supply is considered to comply with Regulation 12(1)(a)?

To be suitable the means chosen must be capable of switching off power quickly enough to prevent danger under all foreseeable circumstances. More specifically it should:

i) be capable of cutting off the supply to the equipment, not only in normal and abnormal operating conditions, but also in fault conditions;

ii) be in a suitable location. The suitability of the location will depend on:

   a) ease of access;

   b) the nature of any risk involved in carrying out the operation;

   c) the speed with which the operation would have to be carried out;

   d) the usual location of the persons who would be required to switch the power off;

iii) be clearly labelled so that there is no doubt about the equipment it controls;

iv) only be common to several different pieces of electrical equipment if it is appropriate to energise and de-energise these as a group.

3.5.14. Isolating equipment: what requirements must be met before the means of isolating equipment are considered to comply with Regulation 12(1)(b)?

To be suitable the means should not only establish an effective electrical barrier between equipment and the power supply but also ensure that no unauthorised person is able to remove that barrier. More specifically it should:

i) establish an air gap between the contacts in the switch or some other barrier which will prevent the flow of current under all conditions of use;

ii) include some device, such as a lock, or provision for a padlock which will prevent the removal of the barrier by anyone but authorised personnel;

iii) be located in such a way that accessibility and ease of operation are appropriate to the task to be performed;

iv) be clearly labelled so that there is no doubt about the equipment which it controls;

v) only be common to several different pieces of electrical equipment if it is appropriate to energise and de-energise these as a group.

3.5.15. The selection of isolator switches

If isolator switches (or disconnectors) are employed to effect isolation they should meet the following requirements.

i)   The barrier established between the isolated equipment and the power source should be either in accordance with an appropriate standard or at least as effective as the requirement set out in the standard.

ii)   Once the barrier has been established it should be clearly visible or clearly and reliably indicated. As a further precaution, there should be some additional indication that the barrier has been successfully established.

iii)   There should be some provision, such as a lock, to prevent anyone but authorised personnel removing the barrier and reconnecting the equipment to the supply.

That completes Unit 5, now attempt the self-assessment questions and end test which follows.

3.5.16. Self - Assessment Question Test

1. SAQ - Isolation of electrical equipment

Use the space below to complete the following statement:

Where equipment must be isolated in order to prevent danger, the duty holder must

_____

_____

_____

_____

2. SAQ - Electrical equipment covered by Regulation 12(3)

Tick the option which completes the following statement correctly.

If the equipment is itself a source of power, Regulation 12(1)

a) does not apply and alternative precautions should be
    taken to prevent danger.

b) applies only if it is reasonably practicable to isolate
    the equipment to prevent danger.

c) applies, but the requirement to secure the isolation
    and separation of the equipment is not absolute.

d) does not apply and alternative precautions to prevent
    danger are not necessary.

3. SAQ - Suitable means of cutting off the supply

In the space below list the factors which should be taken into account when considering the location of the means of cutting off the supply of electricity.

_____

_____

_____

4. SAQ - Suitable means of isolation

What is the essential difference between the devices which are considered suitable for cutting off the supply to equipment and those suitable for isolating equipment from it? Write your answer in the space below.

_____

_____

_____

5. SAQ - Selection of isolator switches

Fill in the missing words in the following statement.

It is recommended that an isolator switch (or disconnector) should not only establish an isolating electrical barrier which is clearly visible but also.................................that the barrier has been successfully established.

1. Response - SAQ Isolation of electrical equipment

The statement should read as follows:

Where equipment must be isolated in order to prevent danger, the duty holder must ensure the disconnection and separation of equipment from every source of electrical energy in such a way that this disconnection and separation is secure.

2. Response - SAQ   Electrical equipment covered by Regulation 12(3)

Tick the option which completes the following statement correctly.

If the equipment is itself a source of power, Regulation 12(1)

a)   does not apply and alternative precautions should be taken to prevent danger.   ✓

b)   applies only if it is reasonably practicable to isolate the equipment to prevent danger.   ☐

c)   applies, but the requirement to secure the isolation and separation of the equipment is not absolute.   ☐

d)   does not apply and alternative precautions to prevent danger are not necessary.   ☐

The correct option is (a). If equipment is itself a source of power, Regulation 12(1) does not apply and alternative precautions should be taken to prevent danger.

3. Response - SAQ Suitable means of cutting off the supply

What factors should be taken into account when considering the location of the means of cutting off the supply of electricity?

Your list should include the following:

i)   any risks involved in operating the device in that location;

ii)   the location of the persons who would normally be expected to switch off the supply;

iii)   the speed with which the action may have to be taken.

4. Response - SAQ Suitable means of isolation

What is the essential difference between devices which are considered suitable for cutting off the supply to electrical equipment and those used for isolating equipment from it?

Devices used to isolate equipment differ from those whose function is simple to cut off power, by having the means to secure the interruption of power against any unauthorised interference, i.e. be capable of being locked off.

5. Response - SAQ Selection of isolator switches

It is recommended that an isolator switch (or disconnector) should not only establish an isolating electrical barrier which is clearly visible but also PROVIDE SOME OTHER INDICATION that the barrier has been successfully established.

3.5.17. Summary Of Key Points

- Because of the way 'cutting off supply' and 'isolation' are defined, a device which meets the requirements of Regulation 12(1)(a), may not meet those set out in Regulation 12(1)(b). However, if it complies with Regulation 12(1)(b) it must also meet the requirements of Regulation 12(1)(a).

- The means chosen to cut off or isolate equipment must be suitable under all foreseeable conditions of use.

- It should be clearly labelled so there is no doubt about which equipment is affected by its operation.

- When an isolating barrier is inserted in a circuit, a clear indication should be provided to show that it has been successfully established.

- The means chosen to isolate equipment should be provided with a security device which will prevent unauthorised use.

3.5.18. End Test

1. Is the requirement of Regulation 4(1) that the system shall be of such construction as to prevent danger subject to the qualification, **so far as is reasonably practicable?**

2. The safety of an electrical system depends upon two basic requirements. What are they?

3. A test meter is used to establish that a system is dead at the point of work. Why is it important to prove it both before and after the test has been carried out?

4. Does Regulation 4 cover both electrical and non-electrical work?

5. How can the withstand properties of electrical equipment be assessed?

6. Why is it important that protective conductors should be so rated that they survive beyond fault clearance time?

7. In what ways can dust entering electrical equipment cause danger?

8. Can the defence outlined in Regulation 29 be used against any alleged breach of Regulation 7?

9. Where plug and socket connections are not rated for making or breaking the maximum load current, what precaution has to be taken?

10. How may the corrosion of a connection in a protective conductor be accelerated?

11. Can Regulation 8 **Earthing or other suitable precautions**, apply to conductors which are not physically connected to an electrical circuit?

12. What are the main advantages of using a power supply which is referenced to earth?

13. If the earthing of an electrical system cannot be guaranteed what additional precautions should be taken?

14. How does the equipotential bonding of all the exposed metal conductors in an area reduce the risk of electric shock?

15. Which circuit conductor is usually earth-referenced?

16. Why is the inclusion of a removable link in the neutral conductor of a circuit permitted by Regulation 9 while a fuse is prohibited?

17. Is the duty, imposed by Regulation 11 to provide effective protection against an excess of current, absolute?

18. How may an excess of current arise?

19. What requirements must a means of cutting off supply meet if it is to be considered suitable for the purposes of Regulation 12(1)(a)?

End Test - Answers

1. Is the requirement of Regulation 4(1) that the system shall be of such construction as to prevent danger subject to the qualification, **so far as is reasonably practicable?**

Yes. The requirement that a system should be of such construction as to prevent danger is subject to the qualification, **so far as is reasonably practicable.**

2. The safety of an electrical system depends upon two basic requirements. What are they?

The safety of an electrical system depends upon among other things:

  i) the proper selection of all electrical equipment used in the system;

  ii) the proper consideration of the inter-relationship between the individual items of equipment.

3. A test meter is used to establish that a system is dead at the point of work. Why is it important to prove it both before and after the test has been carried out?

The only way to be sure that the zero reading indicates that a system is dead, is to prove that the test instrument is functioning in a proper manner both before and after the test is carried out.

4. Does Regulation 4 cover both electrical and non-electrical work?

Yes. Regulation 4 covers both electrical and non-electrical work.

5. How can the withstand properties of electrical equipment be assessed?

The withstand properties of electrical equipment can be assessed using a knowledge of the electrical specifications and tests, carried out either by the manufacturers or by an accredited testing organisation. The specifications and tests are usually based on the requirements of national or international standards.

6. Why is it important that protective conductors should be so rated that they survive beyond fault clearance time?

It is important that any protective conductor survives the flow of a fault current beyond fault clearance time to ensure the satisfactory operation of protective equipment and effective fault clearance.

7. In what ways can dust entering electrical equipment cause danger?

  i) If the dust is combustible it represents a fire hazard.

  ii) If it is conducting it can cause a short circuit with the possible danger of fire and electrocution.

  iii) The dust could increase friction and wear on any moving parts with the consequent danger of overheating and fire.

  iv) A layer of dust on the outside of equipment can prevent normal heat loss and hence lead to overheating.

156

8. Can the defence outlined in Regulation 29 be used against any alleged breach of Regulation 7?

The defence outlined in Regulation 29 CANNOT be used against an alleged breach of Regulation 7.

9. Where plug and socket connections are not rated for making or breaking the maximum load current what precaution has to be taken?

Where plug and socket connections are not rated for making or breaking the maximum load current, arrangements should be made to ensure that connections are only made or broken under no load conditions.

10. How may the corrosion of a connection in a protective conductor be accelerated?

The corrosion of a connection in a protective conductor may be accelerated if combinations of metals are used which react together electrolytically.

11. Can Regulation 8 **Earthing or other suitable precautions**, apply to conductors which are not physically connected to an electrical circuit?

Regulation 8 **Earthing or other suitable precautions**, can apply to a conductor which is not physically connected to a circuit, if it is close enough to the energised conductors to become energised by them.

12. What are the main advantages of using a power supply which is referenced to earth?

An earth-referenced power supply makes it possible to detect earth faults on electrical equipment and automatically cut off the supply.

13. If the earthing of an electrical system cannot be guaranteed what additional precautions should be taken?

Sensitive residual current devices should be used to back up whatever protective measures, (e.g. fuses, circuit breakers), are already in place, if the system earthing cannot be guaranteed.

14. How does the equipotential bonding of all the exposed metal conductors in an area reduce the risk of electric shock?

The equipotential bonding of all the exposed metal conductors in an area, reduces the risk of electric shock, by making it more difficult to be simultaneously in contact with two conductors at different potentials. If the conductors are bonded in this way, should the potential of one be inadvertently raised as the result of a fault, all are raised to the same level. Consequently, anyone touching two or more of them at the same time would not receive an electric shock, so long as they were not similarly in contact with an unbonded conductor at a different potential.

15. Which circuit conductor is usually earth-referenced?

The circuit conductor which is usually earth-referenced is the neutral conductor.

16. Why is the inclusion of a removable link in the neutral conductor of a circuit permitted by Regulation 9 while a fuse is prohibited?

Regulation 9 allows the inclusion of a removable link in the neutral conductor of a circuit while prohibiting fuses because of the degree of risk involved. If the people who work on or with the circuit are competent, there is little risk of the link being removed in circumstances which would give rise to danger. However, a fuse could not be relied on not to blow and create a dangerous open circuit.

17. Is the duty, imposed by Regulation 11 to provide effective protection against an excess of current, absolute?

The duty, imposed by Regulation 11 to provide effective protection, is absolute.

18. How may an excess of current arise?

An excess of current may arise as a result of a short circuit or as a result of the inadequacy of a system to meet the demands placed upon it.

19. What requirements must a means of cutting off supply meet if it is to be considered suitable for the purposes of Regulation 12(1)(a)?

The requirements which must be met by a suitable means of cutting off supply are that it should:

i) be capable of cutting off the supply under all likely conditions;

ii) be readily and safely accessible;

iii) be clearly marked to show its relationship to the equipment it controls.

MODULE FOUR

Introduction

This is the fourth and last module. It covers the requirements set out in Regulations 13 to 15 and is concerned with the procedures necessary to fulfil them.

They cover respectively, the precautions necessary for work on equipment made dead, precautions necessary for work on or near live, uninsulated conductors, and the provision of access, space and light when work takes place in circumstances where danger might arise.

CONTENTS

UNIT 1

4.1.1. Aim

The aim of this unit is to familiarise you with the requirements of Regulation 13 and its implications.

Objectives

When you have worked through this unit you will be able to:

- list the factors which should be considered when selecting equipment or designing systems, to ensure that work on them can be carried out safely;

- explain the role of the person given the task of supervising such work;

- outline a safe working procedure;

- describe the permit to work system.

4.1.2. Overview

This unit is concerned with the requirements of Regulation 13 and the implications of those requirements.

The precautions which should be taken to comply with the Regulation are examined first, followed by a consideration of the rules and procedures which should support them.

We then move from the general to the specific with an outline of a safe working procedure and a detailed review of a permit to work system.

The unit concludes with a reference to the safety aspects of decommissioning electrical equipment.

4.1.3. Regulation 13: Precautions for work on equipment made dead.

Adequate precautions shall be taken to prevent electrical equipment, which has been made dead in order to prevent danger while work is carried out on or near that equipment, from becoming electrically charged during that work if danger may thereby arise.

If work is to be undertaken on or near electrical equipment made dead, it must remain so if danger would result from it becoming charged. The duty imposed by Regulation 13 is absolute. Remember that simply disconnecting the equipment from its usual source of power and ensuring that it cannot be reconnected, may not be enough to comply fully with this Regulation. There are a number of ways whereby equipment can acquire a charge when it is disconnected in this way, and the precautions called for in Regulation 13 must include action to counter this possibility.

The defence outlined in Regulation 29 is available in any proceedings alleging a breach of this Regulation.

If safety is to be assured, a range of precautions are considered to be necessary but, before we look at these, we should consider the consequences of not implementing adequate precautions.

Consequences of the failure to take adequate precautions

About 20 people die as a result of electric shock or burns sustained at work every year. In addition, about 900 electrical injuries are reported to the HSE each year. Probably many more people suffer electric shock but don't report it.

In many cases the victims believed the apparatus they were working on to be dead, or, had used an ineffective means of ensuring that it remained dead while they were working on it. In other cases, it was known that the apparatus was live but it was not considered to pose any danger.

> **Many accidents result from the failure to plan ahead.**

4.1.4. Precautions

The precautions which should be taken to comply with the requirements of Regulation 13 fall into two categories:

i) **Design of systems and selection of equipment:** The careful selection and design of equipment can do much to ensure safety. For example:

   a) isolators should be capable of being secured in the **off** position;

   b) an adequate number of isolation points should be provided;

   c) control panels should be designed with insulated conductors and shrouded terminals so that work can be carried out with the minimum of risk;

   d) interlocking should be used wherever possible, so that equipment is de-energised when, for example, a barrier or cover is removed, so contact with live parts is prevented;

   e) equipment is preferred which has power circuits separated from control circuits and other services such as pneumatic and hydraulic devices .

ii) Supervision: Safe working procedures rely on sound systems of work, carried out by competent and adequately trained personnel.

The degree of supervision provided should be appropriate to the danger present, and the technical knowledge and expertise of the people doing the work. It is preferable that the supervisor should receive written authorisation from his employer. He should:

i) discuss the work with the staff involved and ensure that they understand what precautions are to be taken;

ii) co-ordinate the work of the different teams if more than one is involved;

iii) ensure that everyone knows what is to be done if something goes wrong.

> **Only one person should have overall responsibility and everyone involved in the work should know who it is.**

4.1.5. Procedures and Rules

Wherever electrical work is to be carried out, there should be a system of written rules and procedures. By putting these into writing it is easier to ensure that everyone is made aware of them.

Simplicity of presentation and brevity should always be the aim, but not to the point where there is a danger of ambiguity or the omission of important detail.

The nature and complexity of the work may require that there is more than one document.

The principles and general practice should be set out in a clear and compact form, so that those who need to, can carry a copy with them.

It may be more convenient to set out the detailed procedures which relate to specific items of equipment, in separate documents.

Although it may not be necessary to issue these to everyone, they should be made available to all who may need them as and when they are required (even outside usual working hours).

4.1.6. Recommended Procedure

The varied nature of electrical work makes it impossible to lay down a procedure which would be appropriate for every situation. However, the following sequence is a useful guide. It may require modification to meet the specific needs of particular systems.

i) **Plan the Job:** This should include correctly identifying the equipment and the points of isolation, and the action to be taken if things go wrong.

ii) **Disconnection:** Disconnect the equipment from every source of electrical energy. Remember that these sources do not have to be physically connected to the equipment. The main power source will be, but there may be others capable of transferring energy to the equipment despite the absence of a physical link. Electrical energy may also be stored within it. Although it may be difficult, even impossible, to disconnect these internal sources of energy, the procedure which follows is intended, nevertheless, to prevent danger arising.

iii) Isolation: The means of disconnecting the equipment must be made secure. Switches should be locked off and the key(s) secured. If the disconnection has been effected by removing a plug, the socket should preferably be secured to prevent re-insertion. If a fuse has been removed it must be kept in a secure place, and steps taken to ensure that it cannot be replaced.

iv) Proving: Although the procedure for disconnection and isolation is completed that is no guarantee that the equipment is electrically dead. It must be proved dead before any work can be safely undertaken. The process was briefly discussed in Module 3.1.3.3. Remember the sequence is:

    a) prove the test instrument to show that it is functioning properly;

    b) use it to establish that the equipment is dead;

    c) prove the test instrument again.

v) Earthing: The equipment should preferably be earthed, as an additional precaution against it being re-energised. This is particularly important at high voltages (e.g. 1000 volts). An earth lead should be attached at the point of isolation and also at the point of work, if this is remote from the isolator. The earth leads should be capable of withstanding the flow of any foreseeable current.

vi) Post Notices: Two sets of notices should be displayed in association with the isolated equipment.

    a) CAUTION NOTICES - These should be posted at the place where the equipment is disconnected. They should warn that work is being carried out on the equipment and it would be dangerous to re-energise it.

    b) DANGER NOTICES - These should be used to warn of any adjacent live equipment.

All pictograms should comply with the requirements of the Safety Signs Regulations and indicate their purpose clearly and simply.

When notices are no longer required, they should be removed in order to avoid confusion/misunderstanding which may cause danger.

---

vii) Consider the need for additional precautions: Additional precautions will be needed if there is the risk of making inadvertent contact with the live parts of adjacent equipment. These precautions may take the form of physical barriers or additional, temporary insulation.

viii) Ensure understanding of the job: Do not start work unless there is adequate understanding of the work to be done, the precautions that have been taken, additional hazards that may arise, and the action to be taken in the event of things going wrong.

The Regulation does not preclude the application of a test voltage to equipment provided that this does not give rise to danger.

Recommended Safe Working Procedure

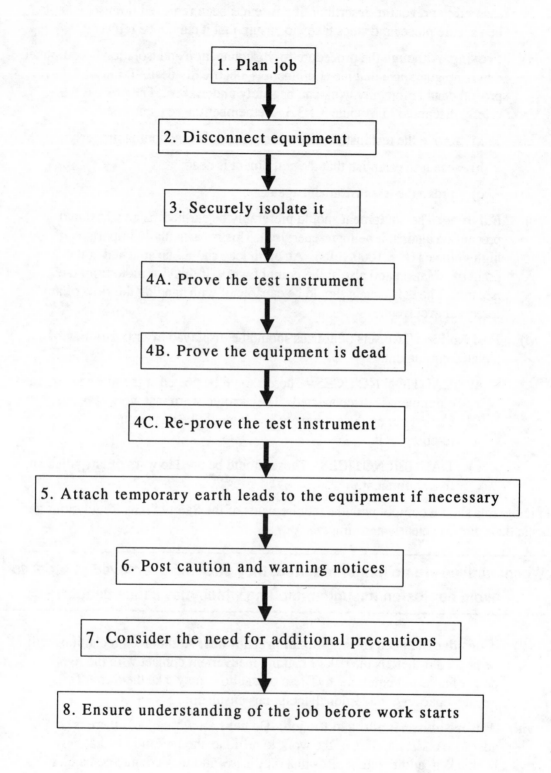

1. Plan job

2. Disconnect equipment

3. Securely isolate it

4A. Prove the test instrument

4B. Prove the equipment is dead

4C. Re-prove the test instrument

5. Attach temporary earth leads to the equipment if necessary

6. Post caution and warning notices

7. Consider the need for additional precautions

8. Ensure understanding of the job before work starts

4.1.7. Permits to Work

A permit-to-work enhances safety by setting down the agreed safe working procedure in writing.

> **It must only be issued for work on equipment made dead.**

The precautions which must be taken are set out in the document together with details of the nature and location of the work.

Usually the person issuing the document is responsible for its content, and so must be technically competent in regard to the equipment and systems covered by the permit to work. He must plan the work and he is responsible for ensuring that the precautions detailed in the document have been taken. In addition, he must also ensure that the person in charge of the work has a clear understanding of the work schedule and all the necessary safety measures.

Once the permit has been accepted and signed by the work supervisor, he takes full responsbility for his own safety and the safety of those under his control. He should retain the document until the work is completed.

Upon completion he must ensure that all the workforce is withdrawn, together with their tools and equipment, and instructed not to return. Any temporary earth connections must also be removed.

The equipment should not be re-energised until the permit is returned to the person who issued it for cancellation.

If it is necessary to alter the work schedule the existing permit must be cancelled and a new one issued.

> **Permits-to-work should never be modified.**

The suspension of permits-to-work is not generally recommended.

However, if it becomes necessary to do so there should be additional documentation to cover the withdrawal of staff and their equipment before the work is completed.

The permit-to-work should be clearly and legibly written to avoid confusion and should contain the following information:

    i)   the identity of the person supervising the work, to whom the permit is issued;

    ii)   sufficient detail to accurately identify the equipment made dead and its location; NB: A diagram will usually ensure that these points are precisely described.

    iii)   the location of the points of isolation;

    iv)   the location of temporary earth connections;

    v)   the location of warning notices and safety locks;

    vi)   a detailed description of the work to be carried out;

vii) an account of other hazards which might be encountered together with any detail necessary to identify them;

viii) further precautions to be taken during the course of the work.

It is essential, if safety is to be assured, that the information contained

in the permit is accurate.

It is strongly recommended that the permit is issued at the place where the work is to be carried out so that the details it contains can be confirmed.

Despite all this, bad habits can develop and a system which theoretically should not fail, can do so with serious consequences. It is essential that any failure should be detected at an early stage and this is best assured by introducing a monitoring system. It is preferable that the person given this duty should be independent of the person issuing the permit and the person receiving it.

The Permit-to-Work Procedure

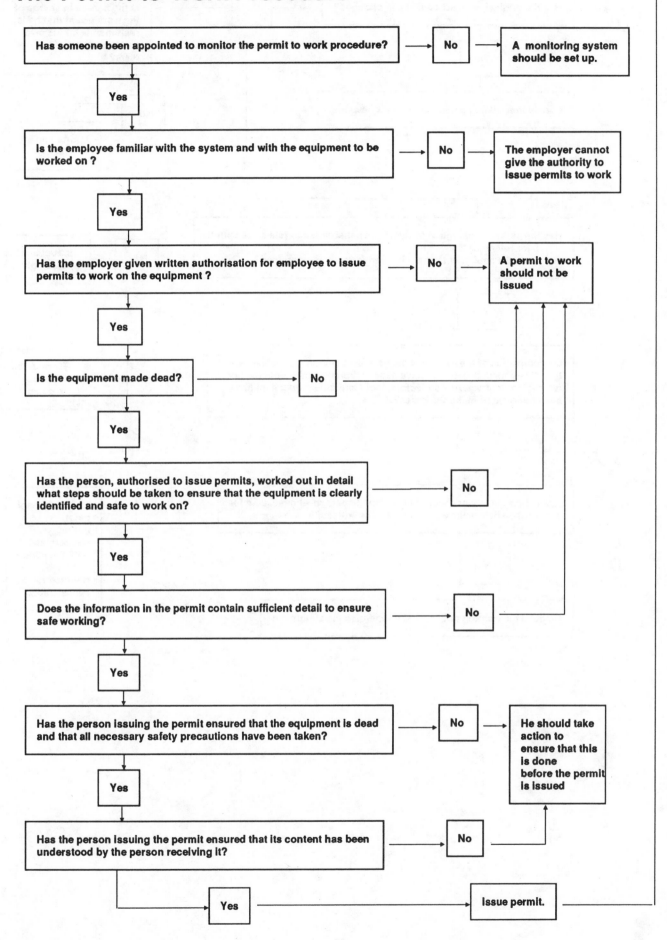

171

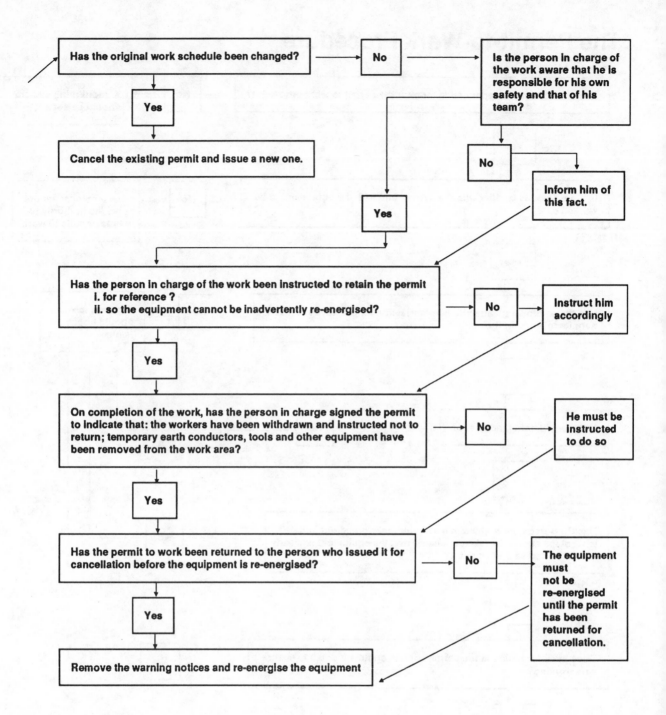

Has the original work schedule been changed?

No

Is the person in charge of the work aware that he is responsible for his own safety and that of his team?

Yes

Cancel the existing permit and issue a new one.

No

Yes

Inform him of this fact.

Has the person in charge of the work been instructed to retain the permit
   i. for reference ?
   ii. so the equipment cannot be inadvertently re-energised?

No

Instruct him accordingly

Yes

On completion of the work, has the person in charge signed the permit to indicate that: the workers have been withdrawn and instructed not to return; temporary earth conductors, tools and other equipment have been removed from the work area?

No

He must be instructed to do so

Yes

Has the permit to work been returned to the person who issued it for cancellation before the equipment is re-energised?

No

The equipment must not be re-energised until the permit has been returned for cancellation.

Yes

Remove the warning notices and re-energise the equipment

4.1.8. Decommissioned equipment

If equipment is taken out of service, for any reason, steps should be taken to ensure that it cannot be a source of danger. This will entail securely isolating it and, if necessary, earthing it so that it cannot be re-energised from any foreseeable source.

Appropriate warning notices or labels should be displayed on or near it.

That concludes Unit 1. The self-assessment question exercise follows.

4.1.9. Self - Assessment Question Test

1. SAQ -   Safety factors to be considered when selecting equipment/designing systems

The careful selection and design of equipment can do much to ensure safety. What recommendations were made in respect of the following features?

Write your answers in the accompanying boxes.

---

a. isolators.

---

b. isolation points.

---

c. control panels.

---

d. interlocking.

---

e. power and control circuits.

2. SAQ - Supervision

a) Complete the following statement.

When discussing the work to be undertaken, with the staff who are to do it, the supervisor should ensure that they:

   i) understand the precise nature of the work they are to do;

   ii) _____

b) How can the supervisor improve safety if more than one team is involved in the work? Write your answer in the space below.

   _____

   _____

   _____

   _____

c) Even in the best organised work programmes things may still go wrong. What should the supervisor do to prepare his team(s) if this should happen? Write your answer in the space below.

   _____

   _____

   _____

   _____

3. SAQ - Recommended safe working procedures

Fill in the gaps in the following sequence.

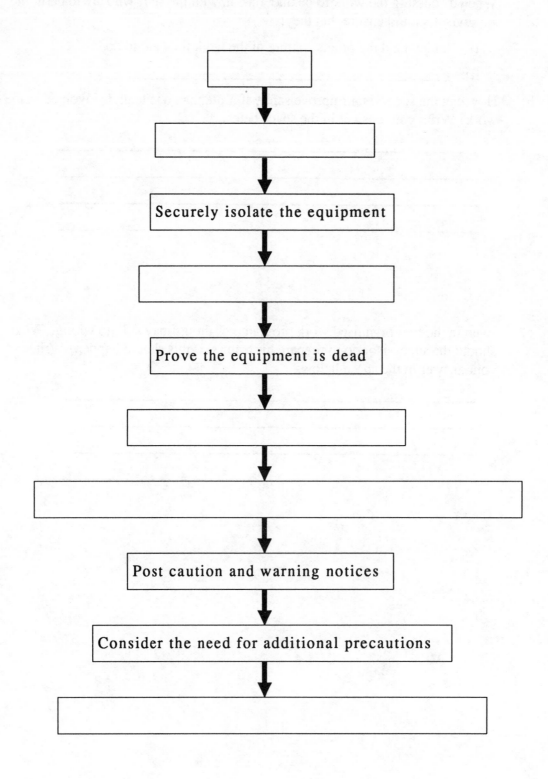

Securely isolate the equipment

Prove the equipment is dead

Post caution and warning notices

Consider the need for additional precautions

4. SAQ - The permit-to-work

Which of the following statements are true. Tick your choice.

a) A permit-to-work can only be issued for work on electrical equipment made dead. ☐

b) A permit-to-work can be issued for work on electrical equipment both live and dead. ☐

c) A permit-to-work can only be issued for work on live electrical equipment if the person issuing the permit is competent to do so. ☐

d) A permit-to-work can be issued for work on electrical equipment both live and dead so long as all the necessary safety precautions have been taken. ☐

1. Response - SAQ - Safety factors to be considered when selecting equipment/designing systems

The careful selection and design of equipment can do much to ensure safety. What recommendations were made in respect of the following features?

Your answer should include the following points.

a) isolators.

Isolators should be capable of being secured in the **off** position.

b) isolation points.

An adequate number of isolation points should be provided.

c) control panels.

Control panels should be designed with insulated conductors and shrouded terminals so that work can be carried out with the minimum of risk.

d) interlocking.

Interlocking should be used wherever possible, so that equipment is de-energised when, for example, a barrier is removed, so contact with live parts is prevented.

e) power and control circuits.

Wherever possible, power and control circuits should be separated.

2. Response - SAQ - Supervision

a) Complete the following statement.

When discussing the work to be undertaken, with the staff who are to do it, the supervisor should ensure that they:

i) understand the precise nature of the work they are to do;

ii) understand what precautions are to be taken.

b) How can the supervisor improve safety if more than one team is involved in the work? Write your answer in the space below.

He should co-ordinate the work of the different teams.

c) Even in the best organised work programmes things may still go wrong. What should the supervisor do to prepare his team(s) if this should happen? Write your answer in the space below.

He should ensure that everyone knows what is to be done if things go wrong.

3. Response - SAQ - Recommended safe working procedures

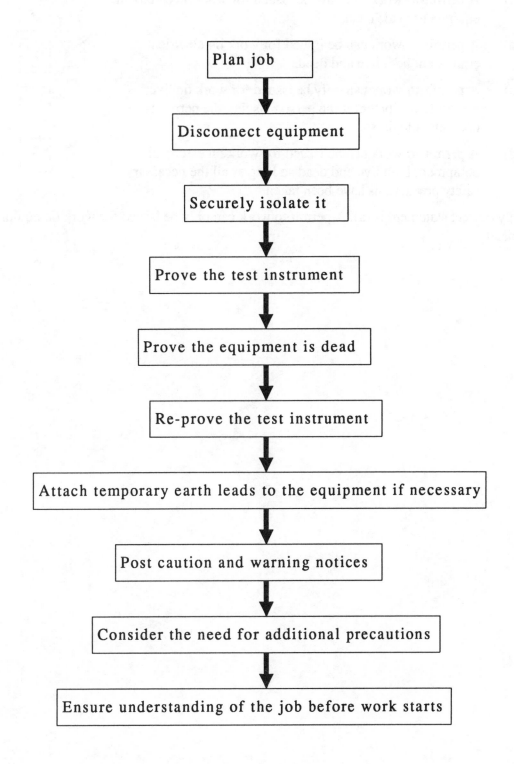

4. Response - SAQ - The permit-to-work

Which of the following statements are true?

a) A permit-to-work can only be issued for work on electrical equipment made dead. ✓

b) A permit-to-work can be issued for work on electrical equipment both live and dead.

c) A permit-to-work can only be issued for work on live electrical equipment if the person issuing the permit is competent to do so.

d) A permit-to-work can be issued for work on electrical equipment both live and dead so long as all the necessary safety precautions have been taken.

The only correct statement is (a). A permit to work can only be issued for work on equipment made dead.

4.1.10. Summary of Key Points

- The duty imposed by Regulation 13 is absolute.

- Disconnecting equipment from its usual source of supply may not be sufficient to meet the requirements of this Regulation.

- Safety can only be assured by planning ahead.

- Safe working procedures rely on sound systems of work.

- When work is undertaken, only one person should have overall responsibility for safety.

- Wherever electrical work is carried out there should be a system of written rules and procedures.

- The minimum precautions which should be taken before work begins on equipment are:

    i)   disconnect;

    ii) isolate;

    iii) prove dead;

    iv) earth;

    v)   post notices.

- The Regulation allows test voltages to be applied to equipment made dead, so long as this does not give rise to danger.

- A permit-to-work system ensures the correct operation of good safe-working procedures.

- Permits-to-work must never be modified. If a work schedule is changed, the existing permit must be cancelled and a new one issued.

UNIT 2

4.2.1. Aim

Regulation 14 stresses the need to switch off before working on or near exposed conductors. It is concerned exclusively with those situations where work must be carried out on or so near live equipment that danger may arise. The aim of this unit is to give you an understanding of what must be done to comply with the requirements of the Regulation.

Objectives

When you have worked through this unit you will be able to:

- set out the questions which should be asked when deciding if live working would be permitted by Regulation 14;

- explain what can be done, either to eliminate the need for live working or reduce the risks associated with it;

- explain the circumstances when work on or close to uninsulated live conductors would be permitted by Regulation 14;

- list the precautions which may be necessary to prevent injury during live working.

4.2.2. Overview

Regulation 14 is concerned with live working. The justification for live working is discussed first followed by a review of the precautions which should be taken if this type of work is unavoidable.

4.2.3. Regulation 14: Work on or near live conductors

No person shall be engaged in any work activity on or so near any live conductor (other than one suitably covered with insulating material so as to prevent danger) that danger may arise unless:

a)   *it is unreasonable in all the circumstances for it to be dead; and*

b)   *it is reasonable in all the circumstances for him to be at work on or near it while it is live; and*

c)   *suitable precautions (including, where necessary, the provision of suitable protective equipment) are taken to prevent injury.*

Regulation 14 recognises that there are instances where the requirements of Regulation 7(a) to cover dangerous conductors with insulating material, cannot be met. Consequently, there will be occasions when work will take place on or so near live conductors that danger will arise.

Regulation 14 is intended to reduce the risk of injury in these circumstances. It is concerned with those situations where work must take place on or near live conductors, whatever the nature of that work might be, which may foreseeably give rise to danger. It is also concerned with those situations where conductors are covered with insulating material but not **suitably covered with insulating material so as to prevent danger**, eg. excavation near underground cables.

The defence outlined in Regulation 29 is available in any proceedings for an offence under this Regulation.

4.2.4. Work on live conductors

Regulation 14 prohibits work on or so near uninsulated live conductors that danger arises, unless the three conditions set out in the Regulation are met. Don't forget danger can arise, even at relatively low voltages.

4.2.4.1. The first of these is, 'unless it is unreasonable in all circumstances for it to be dead'

There are four general circumstances when it may be necessary to work on live, uninsulated conductors.

i)   **When it is not practicable to carry out the work with the conductors dead.**

It may be difficult, if not impossible, to commission a complex control cabinet without having it energised at some time. In these circumstances, work on or near dangerous exposed conductors may be unavoidable.

Similarly, it may not be realistic to monitor the operation and performance of a control system or to trace a malfunction of such equipment with it dead.

ii) **When other hazards might arise as a result of the conductor being made dead.**

> The loss of power may put other users of the system at risk, e.g. the failure of a lifting electro-magnet may give rise to danger. There are many examples of situations where hazards would be created should the electricity supply fail.

iii) **When there is a need to comply with statutory requirements.**

iv) **When there is an important economic need to perform the work and the risk of injury involved can be reduced to an acceptable level.**

> The failure of electric power in a transport system, communications, network, or even in the power supply system itself may have serious economic consequences.

> In such cases circumstances might arise where the condition set out in 14(a) would justify live working provided the contents of 14(b) and 14(c) can also be met.

Reducing the hazards associated with live working at the design, purchase and installation stages of the associated electrical equipment.

If it is known that at some stage during the life of equipment live working may be necessary, appropriate action should be taken to minimise the risks. This can be taken at either the design stage, or at the time when the equipment is selected, or at the installation stage, or at all three.

It may be possible at the design stage to eliminate the need for live work which puts those involved at risk. This might be achieved, for example, by designing equipment housings which segregate parts that may require work, and so provide protection against adjacent parts which may be live.

Design features which eliminate live working hazards or reduce them should be given appropriate weighting when new equipment is being selected.

When planning installation, safety should be given priority so that live working hazards are reduced to an absolute minimum, e.g. ensure that working space and lighting levels are always sufficient to allow safe working.

It must be remembered that when uninsulated conductors are at a high potential, a person may not actually have to be in contact with them to suffer electric shock or burn. Electrical energy can leap across the intervening gap if the difference in potential is large enough.

The nearest approach of any person or object should not be closer than:

0.8 m if the potential is less than 20kV;

1.0 m if the potential is between 20kV and 40kV;

1.4 m if the potential is between 40kV and 80kV;

2.4 m if the potential is between 80kV and 160kV.

Justification for live working

We can summarise the circumstances in which Regulation 14 would permit live working.

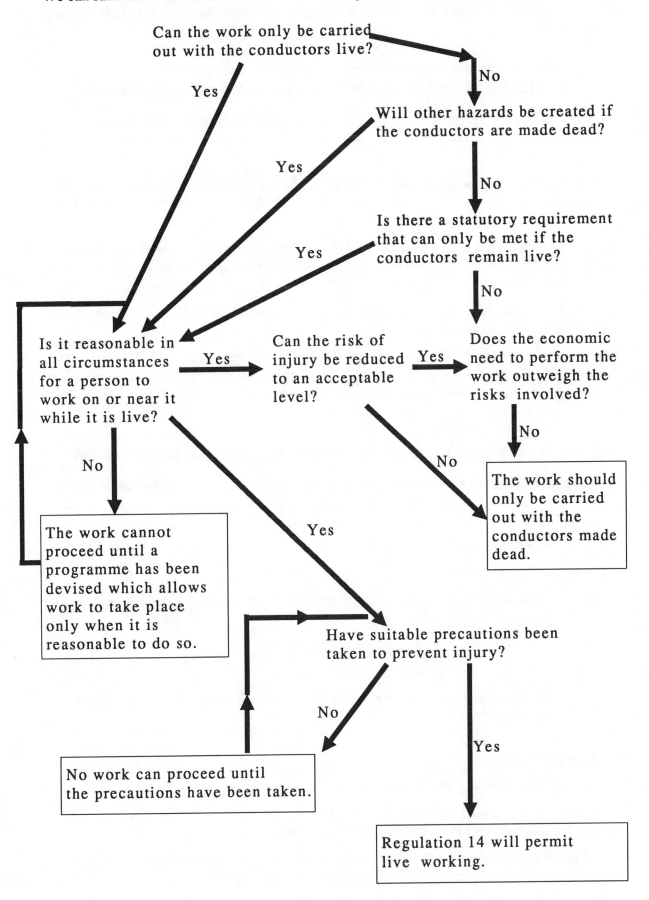

4.2.4.2. The second essential condition Regulation 14 sets out for live working to take place is that 'it is reasonable in all circumstances ... to be at work ... on or near it.'

Before this condition is considered it will have been established that work is permitted while the conductor is live.

> **The justification of live working does not automatically justify the presence of personnel on or near live uninsulated conductors.**

If it is possible to carry work out on the conductors from a distance, e.g. by using specially designed insulated tools, as in power transmission work, then the Regulation would prohibit close working.

It is ONLY when there is no alternative and the work requires a close approach to the live conductor, is it permitted, but then ONLY AFTER ALL NECESSARY PRECAUTIONS HAVE BEEN TAKEN.

4.2.4.3. The third and final condition set by Regulation 14 is that, 'suitable precautions ... are taken to prevent injury.'

The precautions which the Regulation demands must be commensurate with the risks involved. As the degree of risk varies so the precautions required may vary. However this is an absolute requirement to take precautions that are suitable to prevent injury.

> **Regardless of the precautions demanded by particular situations, the basis of all safe working is a sound and well-planned system of work.**

4.2.5. The system of work

The system of work should:

i)   allow only those persons who possess the appropriate competencies to work on or near live conductors;

ii)   indicate clearly the limits set on assigned work;

iii)   make clear what levels of competence are required to carry out the work safely;

iv)   incorporate reporting procedures which will ensure that the limits set are never exceeded.

4.2.6. Precautions

When live working takes place danger cannot be eliminated.

Consequently the purpose of the precautions taken is to prevent injury. The choice of appropriate precautions will be dictated by the circumstances.

    Training: Only people who are properly trained and competent to work on live equipment safely should be allowed to do so.

Information: Those workers involved should be provided with all the relevant information they require to work safely. Information about the exact location, etc. of the conductor is essential if injury is to be prevented.

There is a very real risk of injury to those who are required to excavate in the vicinity of buried cables. It is essential that those involved in such work are aware of the location of the cables and observe good digging practice.

The hazard is clearly visible to those working near overhead power lines but they may be unaware of the danger.

The provision of information which raises awareness of the danger is the first precaution which should be taken.

There are numerous work situations where there may be a risk of making contact with overhead power lines, e.g. working on scaffolding, driving high vehicles such as mobile cranes, moving long metal ladders, etc.

Those involved in work close to underground and overhead power lines can obtain much useful advice from the Health and Safety Executive Guidance:

GS6 Avoidance of Danger from Overhead Electric Lines;

HS(G)47 Avoiding Danger from Underground Services.

The provision of suitable tools and testing equipment: Only properly insulated tools should be used. They should have insulation which is robust enough to be proof against mechanical damage. These tools should be inspected frequently by a suitably competent person.

Test instruments should have insulated probes and fused leads.

If the protective insulation on any tool or item of test equipment is damaged there is a real risk of injury. The damaged equipment should be withdrawn from service and destroyed.

The provision of protective clothing and other protective equipment: Such equipment may include:

- insulated helmets and goggles;
- insulated gloves;
- fixed and temporary insulated screening;
- insulated mats and stands.

It should all be subjected to regular inspection and withdrawn from service and replaced if it is found to be defective.

Accompaniment: Restricting the number of people in the danger area reduces the risk of injury. No one should be allowed to enter it unless their presence is essential.

If the risk of injury can be reduced by being accompanied, (e.g. if there is a risk of electric shock), the person actually carrying out the work should have someone with him. The persons assigned the duty should be capable of recognising danger and giving help should an emergency arise. The help they are able to give may include emergency resuscitation.

It has been shown over the years that rapid action can save life in cases of electric shock.

The Health and Safety (First Aid) Regulations 1981 makes various requirements for the provision of first aid in the work place.

The provision of specially equipped areas for routine testing: Live working often involves electrical testing. Every effort should be made to ensure that the regular testing of live, uninsulated conductors, takes place in a special area. The necessary measures should be taken to ensure that the work can be carried out safely, e.g. provision of isolated power sources, non-conducting environments, etc.

Where tests are required to confirm that apparatus is electrically dead, it must always be assumed that it is live. The testing should only proceed on this assumption, and should be accompanied by all the appropriate precautions.

Restrict entry to the work area: Entry to the work area should be restricted to those personnel whose presence is essential.

That concludes Unit 2. The self-assessment question exercise follows.

4.2.7. Self - Assessment Question Test

1. SAQ - Justification of live working

List the four questions which should be asked when seeking to justify live working. The order of the questions is unimportant.

Write your answers in the space below.

_____

_____

_____

_____

_____

2. SAQ - The elimination or reduction of the risks associated with live working

The need for live working can be eliminated, or the risks attendant on it reduced, before a new system or piece of equipment is energised. At what points are those responsible for the system able to do most to create a safe working environment?

Write your answer in the space below.

_____

_____

_____

_____

_____

3. SAQ - Work on or close to live conductors

Indicate which of the following statements are true and which are false by ringing the appropriate letter.

a)   If there is a risk of contact being made with a live, uninsulated conductor, work on it is not to be permitted by Regulation 14.   T/F

b)   If work can be carried out from some distance away from a live, uninsulated conductor, the same work close to it would not be permitted.   T/F

c)   If a live uninsulated conductor is at a dangerously high potential any work on it would be prohibited by Regulation 14.   T/F

d)   If it has been established that work can only be carried out on uninsulated conductors when they are live, Regulation 14 permits work on or close to them.   T/F

e)   If it has been established that work cannot be carried out on a dead conductor it must also be demonstrated that it is reasonable in all the circumstances for work to be done on or near the conductor while it is live.   T/F

4. SAQ - The precautions necessary to prevent injury

Tick the option which completes the following statement correctly.

A person carrying out work on uninsulated live conductors, should be accompanied

a)   whenever the work being undertaken is dangerous.   ☐

b)   only when there is sufficient space to safely accommodate both workers.   ☐

c)   if, for any reason, it has not been possible to implement the usual precautions.   ☐

d)   if this would contribute to the safety of the person doing the work.   ☐

The answers to these questions begin on the next page.

1. Response - SAQ - Justification of live working

List the four questions which should be asked when seeking to justify live working. The order of the questions is unimportant.

1. Can the work only be carried out with the conductors live?

2. Will other hazards be created if the conductors are made dead?

3. Is there a statutory requirement that can only be met if the conductors remain live?

4. Is there an economic need to perform the work which can be weighed against the level of risk involved in working live and the effectiveness of the precautions available?

2. Response - SAQ - The elimination or reduction of the risks associated with live working

The need for live working can be eliminated, or the risks attendant on it reduced, before a new system or piece of equipment is energised. At what points are those responsible for the system able to do most to create a safe working environment?

There are two points at which steps can be taken to create a safer working environment.

i) The first is when equipment is being selected. Those entrusted with the task should be aware of the nature of the risks and be capable of selecting equipment whose design most significantly reduces them.

ii) The second is at the installation stage. Those who are responsible for planning the installation of the equipment should be aware of the hazards that remain. Their aim should be to design a layout which reduces the risk of injury to a minimum.

3. Response - SAQ - Work on or close to live conductors

Indicate which of the following statements are true and which are false by ringing the appropriate letter.

a) If there is a risk of contact being made with a live, uninsulated conductor, work on it is not to be permitted by Regulation 14.   T/**F**

This statement is false. The Regulation would permit such work, provided that the three conditions set out in Regulation 14 are met and all appropriate precautions are taken.

b) If work can be carried out from some distance away from a live, uninsulated conductor, work close to it would not be permitted.   **T**/F

This statement is true. Although it may be necessary to carry out live working, it may not be equally necessary to work close to the conductor. If techniques are available which obviate the need for close working, anyone who does so is in breach of the Regulations.

c) If a live uninsulated conductor is at a dangerously high potential any work on it would be prohibited by Regulation 14.   T/**F**

This statement is false. See the answer to (a).

d)   If it has been established that work can only be carried out on uninsulated conductors when they are live, Regulation 14 permits work on or close to them.   T/**F**

This statement is false. See the explanation for the answer to b.

e)   If it has been established that work cannot be carried out on a dead conductor it must also be demonstrated that it is reasonable in all the circumstances for work to be done on or near the conductor while it is live.   **T**/F

This statement is true. It is important that the three conditions of Regulation 14 are met before work is done on or near live conductors.

4. Response - SAQ - The precautions necessary to prevent injury

Tick the option which completes the following statement correctly.

A person carrying out work on uninsulated live conductors, should be accompanied

a)   whenever the work being undertaken is dangerous.   ☐

b)   only when there is sufficient space to safely accommodate both workers.   ☐

c)   if, for any reason, it has not been possible to implement the usual precautions.   ☐

d)   if this would contribute to the safety of the person doing the work.   ☑

The correct option is (d). A person carrying out work on uninsulated, live conductors, should be accompanied if this would contribute to his safety.

a)   is incorrect because there is always danger present when live working is undertaken. Accompaniment is not necessary in every case.

b)   is incorrect. The person accompanying does not have to be in the immediate work area.

c)   is incorrect. Work should never proceed if the necessary precautions have not been taken.

4.2.8. Summary of Key Points

The precautions which may be necessary when live working must take place, can be summarised as follows.

- Establish a safe system of work.

- Ensure that personnel are properly trained and competent to carry out the work assigned to them.

- Ensure that they are properly briefed about the nature of the work and the attendant risks.

- Provide tools and equipment which will permit the work to be carried out safely.

- Provide appropriate protective clothing.

- If necessary, take additional precautions such as the placing of insulated barriers, the use of insulated mats, etc.

- Arrange for the person doing the work to be accompanied if this would reduce the risk of injury.

- Restrict admission to the work area to only those staff whose presence is essential.

- Wherever possible, confine routine test work to special areas where precautions can be taken to minimise the risks involved, e.g. isolated power supplies, non-conducting environments, etc.

- Regulation 14 applies to both electrical and non-electrical work.

- All three conditions set out in Regulation 14 must be met before live working is permitted by it.

- The three conditions for live working on a conductor are:

    a) it is unreasonable in all the circumstances for it to be dead; and

    b) it is reasonable in all the circumstances for work to be done on or near it while it is live; and

    c) suitable precautions (including where necessary the provision of suitable protective equipment) are taken to prevent injury.

- There are four general circumstances which may give rise to the need for live working

    i) When it is not practicable to carry out the work with the conductor dead.

    ii) When other hazards might arise as a result of the conductor being made dead.

    iii) When there is a need to comply with statutory requirements.

    iv) When there is an important economic need to perform the work.

- Safety precautions should be backed by a sound system of work.

- If the safety of a worker can be substantially enhanced by being accompanied, then he should be provided with this support.

- Entry to the area where uninsulated, live conductors are located should be restricted to those whose presence is necessary.

- There should be procedures for the periodic inspection and, if necessary, testing of all protective equipment. Any item found to be defective should be replaced.

- The tools and equipment used for work on uninsulated live conductors should be periodically inspected. Any item found to be defective and irreparable should be destroyed.

UNIT 3

4.3.1. Aim

The aim of this unit is to familiarise you with the requirements and implications of Regulation 15.

Objectives

When you have completed this unit you will be able to:

- explain what provision must be made for access, working space and lighting in areas where work must be carried out in circumstances which might give rise to danger.

4.3.2. Overview

Regulation 15 is concerned with the working area. The dimensions of the space which should be available if work is to be carried out safely, and access to it, is considered first.

The provision of adequate lighting is briefly reviewed at the end of the unit.

4.3.3. Regulation 15: Working space, access and lighting

For the purpose of enabling injury to be prevented, adequate working space, adequate means of access, and adequate lighting shall be provided at all electrical equipment on which or near which work is being done in circumstances which may give rise to danger.

The purpose of this Regulation is to ensure that a safe working environment is established whenever work has to be undertaken that may give rise to danger. There are two points to note here.

i)   The Regulation does not only apply to those situations where live working may be necessary, but to any where work is being done in circumstances which may give rise to danger.

ii)   Whilst the provision of suitable access, light and space is only required while work is taking place it should be remembered that almost all those likely to be at the work place will be "at work". The 'danger' envisaged includes danger to those whose work is not concerned with the electrical system.

The defence outlined in Regulation 29 is available in any proceedings for an offence under this Regulation.

4.3.4. Adequate working space

Where there are dangerous uninsulated live conductors in the working area sufficient space must be provided to:

i)   allow persons to move around and pull back without hazard;

ii)   allow persons to pass each other, if the need arises, easily and without hazard.

Regulation 17 of the now revoked Electricity (Factories Act) Special Regulations 1908 and 1944 specified minimum width and height dimensions for switchboard passageways, where there were bare conductors, exposed or arranged to be exposed when live, so that they might be touched. These stated:

a)   low pressure (low pressure: not exceeding 250 volts) and medium pressure (medium pressure: above 250 volts but not exceeding 650 volts) switchboards shall have a clear height of not less than 7 ft (2.1m) and a clear width measured from the bare conductor of not less than 3 ft (0.9m);

b)   high pressure (high pressure: above 650 volts but not exceeding 3000 volts) and extra high pressure (extra high pressure: above 3000 volts) switchboards shall have a clear height of not less than 8 ft (2.4m) and a clear width measured from the bare conductor of not less than 3 ft 6 ins (1.1m);

c)   bare conductors shall not be exposed on both sides of the switchboard passageway unless either (i) the clear width of the passage is in the case of low pressure and medium pressure not less than 4 ft 6 ins (1.4m) and in the case of high pressure and extra high pressure not less than 8 ft (2.4m)in each case measured between bare conductors, or (ii) the conductors on one side are so guarded that they cannot be accidentally touched.

Although they are no longer a statutory requirement these dimensions can still be taken as providing guidance for an appropriate level of safety in many circumstances where the voltages do not significantly exceed 3000 volts.

> **The existence of these guidelines does not condone the use of equipment having exposed conductors if a safe alternative can reasonably be adopted.**

4.3.5. Lighting

Whatever source of light is used it must be adequate to prevent injury occurring.

Natural daylight is to be preferred but where this is not possible, the light should be provided from a fixed and permanent installation.

However, the Regulation recognises that circumstances may arise where this is not possible. In these cases the torches or hand lamps used must still provide adequate and safe illumination.

The Health and Safety Executive's publication HS(G)38 'Lighting at work' contains useful information on appropriate light levels.

4.3.6. Summary of key points

- Adequate access, space and lighting are only required by Regulation 15 while work is actually being carried out on or near electrical equipment, in circumstances which might give rise to danger.

- The work can be work of any kind.

- The provision of adequate space around electrical equipment does not condone the use of exposed conductors if a safe alternative can be adopted.

- Fixed and permanent light sources are preferred, but whatever the source, the level of light provided must be sufficient to allow work to be carried out safely.

That concludes Unit 3. The End Tests which complete this fourth and final module follow.

4.4. End Test - Questions

1. Why may simply disconnecting equipment from its usual power supply be insufficient to comply with the requirements of Regulation 13?

2. Why is it necessary to attach temporary earths to electrical equipment made dead, before work commences?

3. Give examples of THREE of the precautions which might be taken when considering the design of systems and selection of equipment.

4. What factors should be taken into account when deciding the degree of supervision which may be necessary to ensure safety?

5. What TWO steps should precede the testing of equipment to prove that it is dead?

6. What are the two types of notices which it may be necessary to display when work is undertaken on electrical equipment made dead?

7. Does Regulation 13 permit a test voltage to be applied to electrical equipment that has been made dead?

8. Who is responsible for ensuring that the precautions detailed in the permit-to-work have been taken?

9. What must the person who issued the permit-to-work be assured of before he cancels it and re-energises the equipment?

10. How is the permit-to-work affected if the work schedule has to be 'modified'?

11. What should be done to ensure that a permit-to-work system remains effective?

12. Does Regulation 14 apply only to electrical work on or near live, uninsulated conductors?

13. What are the FOUR general circumstances when it may be necessary to work on a live, uninsulated conductor?

14. What are the THREE requirements that must be met under Regulation 14?

15. What should be done to reduce the risks associated with routine live testing?

16. What should be expected of those people who accompany workers carrying out work on live, uninsulated conductors?

17. Does Regulation 15 permit the use of hand-held torches as light sources, when work is being carried out in circumstances which might give rise to danger?

End Test - Answers

1. Why may simply disconnecting equipment from its usual power supply be insufficient to comply with the requirements of Regulation 13?

This may not be sufficient if the equipment may be energised by some other means.

2. Why is it necessary to attach temporary earths to electrical equipment made dead, before work commences?

If the equipment is inadvertently re-energised, the current will be harmlessly discharged to earth.

3. Give examples of THREE of the precautions which might be taken when considering the design of systems and selection of equipment.

Your answer should include three of the following:

Isolators should be capable of being secured in the off position.

An adequate number of isolation points should be provided.

Control panels should be designed with insulated conductors and shrouded terminals so that work can be carried out with the minimum of risk.

Interlocking should be used wherever possible.

It is preferable that power circuits should be separated from control circuits and other services.

4. What factors should be taken into account when deciding the degree of supervision which may be necessary to ensure safety?

The degree of supervision should be appropriate to the danger present, and the technical knowledge and expertise of the people doing the work.

5. What TWO steps should precede the testing of equipment to prove that it is dead?

The two steps are:

i) disconnection of the equipment from every source of energy;

ii) isolation; the means of disconnecting the equipment must be made secure.

6. What are the two types of notices recommended to display when work is undertaken on electrical equipment made dead?

The two types of notices are:

i) caution notices;

ii) danger notices.

7. Does Regulation 13 permit a test voltage to be applied to electrical equipment that has been made dead?

Yes, so long as there is no resulting danger.

8. Who is responsible for ensuring that the precautions detailed in the permit-to-work have been taken?

The person who issued the permit should ensure that the precautions have been taken.

9. What must the person who issued the permit-to-work be assured of before he cancels it and re-energises the equipment?

He must be assured by the person who carried out the work that all personnel have been withdrawn from the area covered by the permit, together with all their equipment and any temporary earth conductors.

10. How is the permit-to-work affected if the work schedule has to be 'modified'?

The permit should be cancelled and a new one re-issued which incorporates the modifications.

11. What should be done to ensure that a permit-to-work system remains effective?

The system should be monitored, preferably by someone independent of both the person who issues the permits and those who carry out the work.

12. Does Regulation 14 apply only to electrical work on or near live, uninsulated conductors?

No. The Regulation applies to any work carried out on or near live, uninsulated conductors, regardless of its nature.

13. What are the THREE general circumstances when it may be necessary to work on a live, uninsulated conductor?

The general circumstances are:

i)   when it is not practicable to carry out the work with the conductor dead;

ii)   when other hazards might arise as a result of the conductor being made dead;

iii) when there is need to comply with statutory requirements;

iv)   when there is an important economic need to perform the work.

14. What are the THREE requirements that must be met under Regulation 14?

a)   It must be unreasonable in all the circumstances for the conductor to be dead.

b)   It is reasonable in all the circumstances for work to be done on or near the conductor while it is live

c)   Suitable precautions (including where necessary the provision of suitable protective equipment) are taken to prevent injury.

15. What should be done to reduce the risks associated with routine live testing?

If possible, the work should be restricted to a specific area where precautions have been taken to eliminate or reduce the risks, such as the provision of isolated power supplies and non-conducting areas, etc.

16. What should be expected of those people who accompany workers carrying out work on live, uninsulated conductors?

Those in the accompanying role should be capable of recognising danger and able to render assistance should the need arise.

17. Does Regulation 15 permit the use of hand-held torches as light sources, when work is being carried out in circumstances which might give rise to danger?

Yes, so long as the level of light provided is sufficient to allow the work to be carried out safely.

5.1. Concluding End Test

Typical problems:	What regulations are applicable?
1. Taped joints.	
2. Cord grip not connected.	
3. Broken plug/socket and switchgear.	
4. Portable tool not earthed.	
5. Plug fuse replaced by screw.	
6. Live terminals exposed on test bench.	
7. Unprotected probes on test lamp.	
8. Cable not protected by conduit or conduit broken.	
9. Cable held in socket by match sticks.	
10. Multi-socket adapter in use in single outlet.	
11. Evidence of overheated cable/apparatus.	
12. TV repairs undertaken without isolating transformer and earth-free area.	
13. Domestic appliances being tested with exposed conductors.	
14. Damaged or perished conductor insulation.	
15. Inadequately experienced/trained person doing electrical work.	
16. Power washer in garage.	
17. Crane working under overhead power lines.	
18. Standard electrical fittings in use in vehicle inspection pit in garage.	
19. Electrician working on overhead crane wires with the power off but no permit or lock off system.	
20. Electrician working in switch room with handlamp and only 18" between panels.	
21. Temporary wiring or loose cable runs.	
22. Contact with underground cable.	

Response - Concluding End Test

Typical problems:	EAW Regulations Applicable
1. Taped joints.	10
2. Cord grip not connected.	10
3. Broken plug/socket and switchgear.	4(2)
4. Portable tool not earthed.	4(1) or 8
5. Plug fuse replaced by screw.	11
6. Live terminals exposed on test bench.	14
7. Unprotected probes on test lamp.	14
8. Cable not protected by conduit or conduit broken.	7
9. Cable held in socket by match sticks.	10
10. Multi-socket adapter in use in single outlet.	5
11. Evidence of overheated cable/apparatus.	5
12. TV repairs undertaken without isolating transformer and earth-free area.	14
13. Domestic appliances being tested with exposed conductors.	14
14. Damaged or perished conductor insulation.	7
15. Inadequately experienced/trained person doing electrical work.	16
16. Power washer in garage.	8
17. Crane working under overhead power lines.	14
18. Standard electrical fittings in use in vehicle inspection pit in garage.	6
19. Electrician working on overhead crane wires with the power off but no permit or lock off system.	13
20. Electrician working in switch room with handlamp and only 18" between panels.	15
21. Temporary wiring or loose cable runs.	7
22. Contact with underground cable.	4

Produced from camera ready copy supplied by Department
Printed in the United Kingdom for HMSO
Dd293852 8/91 C50 G3390 10170